Stinkerbelle

THE NARK

Stinkerbelle
THE NARK

Marna Fyson

London
MICHAEL JOSEPH

First published in Great Britain by Michael Joseph Ltd
52 Bedford Square, London, W.C.1
1976

ISBN 0 7181 1455 8

Set and printed in Great Britain by
Hollen Street Press, Slough, Berks
and bound by Dorstel Press, Harlow, Essex

To
John Forbes Fyson

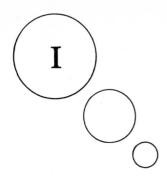

I

Stinkerbelle the Nark complained – a short irritated whine as I rapped the bulge at the bottom of my bed. Half an hour before she had been eager enough to bounce up and follow me downstairs for the first half of her breakfast fish. Having eaten, she had rushed upstairs to snuggle down in my bed again. I thought of the extra twenty-five minutes' sleep she had managed to get and gave the bulge another smart thwack, 'Otter out!'

She complained again and as I uncovered her she looked at me rather malevolently before trying to worm under the pillow. I tugged her back, straightened her out and ignoring her bad temper rudely shoved her on to the floor and kept shoving until we were outside at the edge of her pool. Here, before she had time to recover enough to go scatting upstairs again, I picked her up and unceremoniously gave her a wake-up dunking.

Five minutes later, dry again and much livelier, she bossily demanded the rest of her breakfast. She was eating it as I led my bicycle from the back garden, through the house and out to the front. It was seven o'clock on a summer's morning in London.

My park slacks were on and my gumboots because it had rained hard in the night : a real mid-summer deluge. I next put on my ancient otter coat which was the only coat I've ever had that kept anything out, including otters; its tough woollen material was nicely redolent of such animals. I buttoned it up, found Stinkerbelle's long lead, four dog ones hooked together, and put it in the bicycle basket together with a towel, the end of which I folded over the handlebar brake because once she put her paw between handle and bar just as I squeezed and she limped for three days afterwards.

By the time I got back to the kitchen the otter was curled up in her warm little nest in the ex-pot cupboard. '*Out! Rally!*' The tone used was the equivalent of an English girls' boarding-school gym mistress. Stinkerbelle said, 'Errh', but under some encouragement from my foot swam out of the blankets and onto the floor, where her front paws stretched out front, her back paws stretched out back, her back went concave, her head came up and she gave an immense yawn.

'Come on! We haven't got all day!' Reluctantly, she sat upright on her rump facing her tail and began grooming herself. Then she noted my otter coat and my gumboots. 'Quick!' I said as I went over to the bathroom and kicked her spraint tray. I didn't want to get half way across Richmond Park and find that she wanted to go home to spraint in her very own toilet tray. On finicky feet she slowly padded over to the bathroom.

When she was finished, I took her harness off the door knob, but on hearing the buckles rattle she hastily dived back into the pot cupboard. I grabbed her tail, swung her out and got my hand under her stomach at the same time. The groans of a long-suffering and irate otter filled the room while my voice expressed no nonsense. 'And what on *earth* are you complaining about, for heaven's sake. We're going for a walk! You ungrateful piece of work!' Or some such variation, with much reassurance after the roaring bits.

The harness was one long leather strap which made two rings, one in front of her front paws, one behind them. Her head was not large enough in relation to her neck to allow for a single dog-collar type. I arranged it round her while standing on one foot and somehow balancing her on one raised knee; I'd discovered after much trial and error that she was less likely to fight and generally carry on when faced with her harness if it were put on her while she was off the ground.

Excited squeaks replaced the groaning complaint as soon as the lead was clipped to the buckle. She rushed past me to the front door, put her front paws in the crack, tugged, got the draught cover off, com-

8

plained when I footed her out of the way so I could open the door, then bounced out, leading me to the bicycle where she stood up against the wheel, pippily squeaking, impatiently waiting to be lifted up and put in the front basket. We always bicycled to the park, because although it was only a few minutes walk away, the Nark preferred to be chauffeured there rather than get her soft paws cracked on the asphalt.

She held on to the top of the fence as I straightened up the bicycle. There was a moment when her length was stretched out between fence and basket. The moment passed and we were off, Stinkerbelle hanging her paws over the front while her whiskery face pushed forward sniffing the air. Then she turned around to face me with her paws on the handlebars and we rode along like that until she decided to do her balancing act on the rim. The bicycle wobbled as she got growled at and shoved in again. Fortunately, she responded obediently to the warning note in my voice.

Cars slowed up as they passed; Stinkerbelle squeaked and peered

back intently at the occupants. But soon we were on a quiet park road which led to a bridge crossing a small water course. Here she was tipped out and the long lengths of lead were attached to the short one while she yawned, stretched, turned over, rubbed her back on the grass and generally got ready.

But she was slow at first: that fastidious, pussy-footed waddle again. Anyone looking on would exclaim, 'Poor little thing!' thinking she was sore-footed and feeling sickly. She was neither. Yet as she sniffed the water she managed to look huffy and sullen at the same time, thinking perhaps of her nice cosy blanket in the pot cupboard. Alternately nagging and coaxing, I managed to move her about ten yards in five minutes.

The water course was gushing brim-full after the rain and Stinker-belle was still rather resentfully deciding whether or not to brave it. 'Well, get in!' I said and gave her a shove. She kept to the bank at first, carefully feeling the strength of the current, then more courageously she was in midstream, swimming down fast, dolphining in the deeper pools, her body well adapted to give the least resistance to water with its small ears and general streamlined shape. Her back paws, soles upwards, tucked in one on either side of the base of her tail, then came a hump up as she pulled with her forepaws and down she went.

Under water now, front paws reaching out to explore mud banks or stones, then up again for a dog paddle, her head just above the surface; front paws paddling while the back ones tucked in once more and her tail made a twisty side to side movement all of its own, adding to the forward momentum in much the same way as a sculling oar.

But suddenly a dive, then a rapid swirl to a stop under a bank as she chased a stickleback. Her tail acted as a strong rudder to force her round as her back legs stretched out and webbed paws helped in the braking motion. Almost immediately she started feeling in the soft mud with those sensitive 'fingers' which, unlike other types of otter, had no real claws to get in the way, and soon the stickleback was dislodged. Another mercurial swirl and she had it trapped under the bank in shallower water – a position from which, with paws to help, she could make sure of getting it into her mouth. With head well back she crunched it up with lusty relish.

The water course ran into a stream at the lower end of the park. After the heavy rain it was too full for her. She dithered around the edge, deciding that such a fast-flowing expanse was too dangerous. Actually it was not too bad so I gumbooted in to show her how deep it wasn't and got a gumboot full of water. The Nark stayed on the bank.

Any English *Lutra lutra* otter of course would have plunged into such water with little hesitation, but Stinkerbelle, an *Amblonyx cinerea* or Asian short-clawed, was more careful. Smaller than a *lutra*, she knew her limitations and didn't like to feel water taking her at a speed beyond her control.

Willows hanging over the stream were green and fresh; grass grew high on either side, cobwebs sparkled. I emptied my gumboot and Stinkerbelle had a back scratch before we set off across a large field and up towards a chestnut grove where narrow paths wound through high, sweet-smelling bracken. Crows kraa-ed from the wide spread of summer trees and high above us a kestrel hovered. A red deer stag lifted its head to watch us pass and rabbits flipped white tails as they scatted for cover. The buzz of London traffic was absorbed by green vista and ancient oak as the park shepherdess, with her dogs, herded her flock across the scene, adding a touch of pastoral convention to the rustic aspect of undulating field and woodland.

The bleat of lambs to ewes could be heard as Stinkerbelle galloped along at a cracking pace, bounding off her back feet in a quick one-two time. Her webbed, rubbery feet bounced up to land just behind her front paws, almost meeting them, while her tail was held in a slightly curving arc, tip held just above the ground. Every now and then, however, we stopped so that she could roll in her favourite rolling spots; usually a mixture of dry earth and leaf at the base of certain old oaks.

In this manner and after some more forest we eventually came to the Pen Ponds. They were really small lakes, one set higher than the other; bulrush, tussock and here and there trees around the edges. There was a small willow island in the lower pond.

Stinkerbelle got busy in the bulrushes, working her way slowly, importantly, around the edge until she heard a dog bark, probably one of the shepherdess's dogs and quite far away, but taking no chances she stopped concentrating on the bank to dog paddle instead, head out, ready to chase off any innocent hound which might splash into her pond. In fact, she was so busy thinking about possible interruptions that she didn't notice the large pike lying in the shallows. The fish saw her first, made a loud, splashy swirl and was off to deeper waters. At the same instant, Stinkerbelle, in a panic of self-preservation leapt out of the water. Then she had to be petted and told it was only a fish for goodness sake! and that if she'd been minding her own business she probably would have caught it.

Unconvinced, she returned cautiously and I let her dawdle along while I looked at the morning's wildfowl: the mallard duck, which the day before had four ducklings following her, now had only two; hungry crows, kestrels and foxes take their toll. A pair of cheeky-looking tufted duck admonished us. There was a widgeon out there which was fairly unusual and one of the crested grebes which had nested near the willow tree island. Moorhens went scattering noisily over the lake surface and the coots were there too; black with their little white beak visors and metallic tup-tup warning-off cries.

But the otter, ignoring all wildfowl, went on exploring the edges of bank and the labyrinth of rushes, unperturbed by the visit we got from two large Canadian geese who came closer, irritably honking at her. After one cursory glance she snubbed them although they followed us, complaining loudly, until we skirted the lower lake and climbed up to the top one. Stinkerbelle liked swimming in this straight, shallow stretch so we made good progress as I walked along the edge holding the end of her long lead, while she swam abreast.

At the far end of this upper lake, however, a fence had been built out into the water to stop people disturbing the wild life in a swampy, high reed section surrounded by a semi-circle of woodland and a thick growth of rhododendrons. Stinkerbelle always wanted to swim around the fence, which meant I had to coax or drag her out of the water depending on whether she felt obstinate or cooperative.

This time I dragged. Her mood of mulish dissent was expressed by a lumpish sprawl in which her whole body, including her head and tail, got firmly flattened on the ground. A soured-off look came over her face and that recalcitrant groan of hers sounded worse than usual. If I slackened the lead, she immediately went bounding off in the direction of the water. If I pulled her the way I wanted to go, she spread-eagled herself again which was most embarrassing if anyone happened in the vicinity for it looked as though I was nastily trying to drag a moribund otter around like a flabby lump of dead cod.

It was no use at all trying to yank her along with me, nor did it do a bit of good to yell, talk sharply or in any way show my exasperation. I learnt such things by practised compromise. Instead of doing all the things I might have *felt* like doing, like giving her a good clout or some such, I had to bend down, stroke her and above all *talk* her into my point of view. I had to carefully, calmly and reasonably explain to her why I myself could not follow her and swim with her round that bit of fence, that I was sure she would understand, so 'Come on now, you little Nark!' I said in my kindest, most encouraging and friendly voice. And at last she agreed to follow me, albeit straining sideways until I got her on the path leading around the copse, whereupon she rushed ahead knowing that the way led to the other side of the lake.

We passed the tall sedge grass where, one morning very early, we saw a big fox emerge from the woods, to stand poised and intent in the early morning light. A brief glance of a fine head as he turned towards us, then the lithe movement as he disappeared into the undergrowth.

Stinkerbelle liked this side of the lake. There were deep pools near the banks gnarled with roots and a willow tree calmly drooped like a Chinese sketch at the edge of its reflection. At one deeper pool Stinkerbelle stopped and carefully examined the bank. For here one morning, she caught a fourteen-inch pike. An exciting moment: there was the otter swimming strongly under the water at the end of her long lead, there was I, keeping up with her when, suddenly, a furious dolphining, arching, twisting, diving, a swirl into the bank and she had the pike trapped against the side.

She bit into it, carried it out, then cleverly shifted it well away from the water's edge where it flapped desperately among the leaves. I thought to put it out of its misery but, seeming to swell with importance and self-absorption, she kept warning me off. One doesn't ignore such warnings, so I sat back and watched her nose and paw it around until, when it was still at last, she started in at the tail end, eating so ravenously one would have thought she hadn't eaten for days.

It was more than she could manage though; about two inches of the body and head were reluctantly left on the bankside. The next day she searched avidly for the remains of it. The day after she had a good look round. Even now, a week or so later, she had a little sniff to make sure there was really none left.

A jet lumbered low overhead towards Heathrow. For a moment the sky was cracked, torn open with the sound, but Stinkerbelle, used to the noise, galloped on towards high ground and a small water hole or pond depending on the rainfall. This time it was a real pond. Oak trees surrounded us. It was quiet and secluded here, yet one had a nice view of the Pen Pond lakes. Bracken and tussock stretched away across to the forest. There was a summer sheen of purple on burnt sienna to the grasses and the gold of tussock was supported by the deep greens of rain-washed swamp grass.

As soon as the squirrels had raced up vertical trunks or balletted away along the branches, I sat down at the base of our resting oak, while Stinkerbelle began to explore a well-known burrow. A few seconds later a spray of earth and leaves started flying out of the hole. The earthy nark backed out, still scuffing. Once out, she had a good roll and scratch, swivelling from side to side, front paws up in the air, back legs flat. Her front half moved fast, but her stern stayed relatively still. Then she turned over on her stomach, sighed, relaxed, but remained watchful.

Some minutes later she sat up, with a worried, inquiring look on her face. Standing now, she was balanced on back feet and tail base, front paws held up at right angles to the body as her head turned from side to side. She squeaked-chirped softly. I still hadn't heard anything, but when I got up I saw a horse and rider disappearing between distant trees. 'It's all right,' I said and she relaxed down again.

I was always amazed at the way Stinkerbelle saw things. Stand very still even a few yards away and she would have difficulty making you out; in fact, you'd call her helplessly myopic. But if you moved an inch, the recognition would be immediate.

After a rest, Stinkerbelle explored the little pond, every now and then pulling herself out of the water to run along floating logs, or stopping to lick her paws after a particularly muddy bit of digging, finding perhaps some necessary minerals in this way. She caught four sticklebacks which she ate and two newts which she pawed up to the side and left for me to put back in again. Her head trailed weed as she swam.

The lead was long enough for me to stand well away on the bank and watch her explore. I would have liked to have let her off the lead here, especially when nobody was about, but I had been given permission to walk her in the park on the condition that she was kept on a lead, so it stayed on. By now, however, she was so accustomed to it that the only time she seemed to realise it was there was when we had those small differences of opinion about which direction should be taken. We had one of these small differences as I urged her out of the pool, then coaxed her over to the beginning of the water course which led down from the Pen Ponds.

Here she was content again, for in the first deeper section near the culvert she fished out her long suffering frog. Once she had dug it out of its muddy retreat, she batted it downstream, chased it, caught it, let it go, pulled it round by one leg, swam upstream with it and chased it down once more. This time she stuffed it back under the bank in order to enjoy digging it out again. The frog was beginning to look tired of it all. 'All right Stinkerbelle,' I said, 'leave the poor thing!'

Sunlight flickered over stretches of water, her whiskers sparkled and her coat had a silvery sheen when the light caught it and I thought how such a system of whiskers must act as antennae under the water, feeling the movement of underwater creatures and currents. Then I wondered about the reason for the whitish patch under her chin, graduating down to the greyish-white section of her chest; perhaps in the water this acted as a light and shadow camouflage, protecting her from any predator which might attack from underneath, or possibly she had these light patches on her because it would make it easier for otters to locate one another's movements in the dark. Then she climbed out and dried herself off on the bank and I had to stand there and wait.

Not for long though, for she got dry very quickly; the long, outer, waterproof guard hairs soon looked glossily dry. They were chocolatey-brown in colour with an ashy sheen. The soft whitish fur packed tightly underneath was as guaranteed to keep out water as duck's down. Only the very tip of her tail remained wet-looking.

On the way back, Stinkerbelle alternated swims with rolls on the bank or digs under it until, all at once, we both stopped. She stood upright again, turning her head, sniffing the air, squeaking as she stared at the animals in front. The smell excited her and I held her back as a herd of the small fallow deer crossed the field and came down to the water course. As they bounded over the water, their legs tucked under them for an instant. It reminded me of ancient cave paintings. Then off they went, some using that deliberate rather stiff-legged gait, others a stotting little run as they moved away towards the forest. When they had crossed, Stinkerbelle stopped to sniff at their traces after which she stood up again on her hind feet watching them go.

But we were on the home stretch now. I could see my bicycle parked by the small tree down by the bridge where we started off on our circuitous route. It was still a fair way to go however and Stinkerbelle who knew we were on the home stretch decided on a go-slow. She messed around in every pool, swirled back against the current, wedged herself under banks, tried to get lost in the rushes, was determined to fish out yet another frog or stickleback. Getting impatient, I tried to talk her into coming out on the bank, having a roll, then a nice little gallop, but she wasn't having it. She disappeared in a bunch of water-cress. I was wondering if I should pick her up and carry her a while to let her know who was boss, when suddenly I saw something in the distance and knew I wouldn't have to.

I gave Stinkerbelle's lead a tweak. 'I say, Stinkerbelle, look!'

She looked up. 'Come out *quick!*' I said. Catching the excitement in

my voice, she came quickly up on to the bank. As soon as she was up there she saw what I saw, because it was moving fast in our direction. She tensed. I held her close, patting her. Then he came nearer, one of those park runners, dressed in nice conspicuous white and making a good cantering pace down our home stretch in the general direction of my bicycle.

It couldn't have been better timed! As he came nearer, I bent down holding Stinkerbelle firmly in case she did her little bound forward with her high-pitched attack screech; frightful enough to scare any runner out of his stride. He passed, feet echoing and thudding on the ground just in front of us. I took a deep breath, let the lead out and was off! Stinkerbelle did give a bit of a screech. The runner glanced back over his shoulder and ran faster. Stinkerbelle had that grimly determined, purposeful look on her face. She hated people to be walking in front of her in the park and she loathed the thought of a runner, so she was galloping along after him, straining at her lead, determined he shouldn't get away. We were moving fast. I was getting breathless. The faster the runner sprinted on, the faster Stinkerbelle galloped. The ground thudded. The runner kept looking back over his shoulder. And so we paced him down the straight doing in five minutes what would otherwise have taken us half an hour.

Level with my bicycle, I hauled Stinkerbelle round and talked to her while the runner disappeared. She had her last dip in the water course, then got out, rolled herself dry on her towel, was lifted into the bicycle basket and with the ten a.m. sun well up in the sky and the sky blue between packs of cloud, we cycled home.

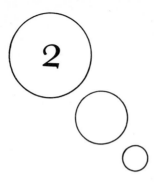

2

Before my husband Forbes and I had arrived in London from Bangkok with an otter in tow, we had thought, 'Ah, masses of cheap fish: sprats, herrings, eels, cod, whiting and so on.' At that time, we didn't know it was bad policy to give an otter too much sprat and herring, for these fish contain a substance called thiaminase which could have a destructive effect on necessary vitamin B complexes.

Stinkerbelle did though; she turned up her nose in disgust at sprats, was absolutely disgusted at the limpness and lethargic look of herrings, tried the mackerel, found it wanting and thought it should have been obvious to us that whiting was only fit for low status cats. Cod she tried and managed after a long, hard effort to get a piece down, then thought she might as well starve now as later. Haddock had met with the same fate.

Seemingly, Stinkerbelle could not understand why we wouldn't supply her with her usual fresh, crunchy fish, small crabs and shrimps which she had been used to in Thailand. But by this time we were getting a bit sick of eating up all her old fish so we said, 'All right Stinkerbelle, *starve*, bother you!' and went out and bought ourselves a couple of juicy rump steaks.

I put them lovingly down on the kitchen table and had just turned to deal with the intricacies of the stove when suddenly I heard a chomping noise behind me: the Nark, leaning her elbows on the table was gnashing down steak.

Now Stinkerbelle had never eaten meat before. Charlie, her Thai mate had, but Stinkerbelle had always looked at it as if it were the last sort of insult. That was when we were living in Bangkok though. Scottish rump steak was different. I got half of it back because I thought it would be too much of a good thing for her to eat it all in one go. We shared the other and she ate the rest of hers later. We were beginning to understand where we stood.

The next day a pound of lean stewing steak was bought and Stinkerbelle munched her way through most of that with the satisfied look gourmets have when eating their favourite dishes. But she ought to have some roughage we decided, so we found a couple of well-stocked fish shops and started experimenting again.

Of course we knew she liked trout. She adored trout, it was her favourite fish, but we were quite firm about how often she got it. She got eels more frequently and enjoyed those too. Then we went on to Barbados flying fish until we discovered she enjoyed plaice and dabs which are cheap in comparison and have enough bone and rough skin for crunching, grinding and roughage purposes.

But during this summer when walking her in the park, I kept seeing fishermen both young and old out with their rods and looking exceedingly serious about it.

So the next time I went to buy my pet owl's fly cocoons at the local fish tackle shop, I said to the owner 'If you know of anyone who catches so many fish he doesn't know what to do with, or any small boys who want to sell them, then please let me know.' I gave him my number and hopefully waited.

A few days later the telephone rang. 'Look, I've got a bucketful here. Do you want them?'

It was just on evening. I'd been trying to make a shelf in the kitchen in between tiling the shower base and doing some hopeful repair work on wood rot, for instead of buying a small flat in the centre of London which would have been easier for us, we had bought this tiny Georgian, semi-detached load of work because being near Richmond Park it was more convenient for Guess Who and her daily walks.

Forbes had had to fly off to the other side of the world to consult on fishing boats which was why the shelf wasn't quite straight and the tiles had a tendency to drop off. The kitchen was full of tools, paint-pots, birdseed, bits of Stinkerbelle's fish tails, toys, half a bag of cement and a bag of sand not to mention other odds and ends. It wasn't particularly neat and tidy and from their kitchen perches a couple of Senegalese yellow-bellied parrots loudly screeched at the two young men edging in to put down their bucket.

'Oh! They're . . . Good heavens!' I said.

'Thought you wanted them alive,' they said.

'Yes, well – er – marvellous!' watching dozens of smallish fish darting around in the bucket. 'Yes, she'll love them,' I added. My two visitors were looking around them as if they couldn't imagine how anyone could live in such a combination of workshop and hash joint, not to mention share it with two parrots and an otter and didn't you say an owl? when suddenly Stinkerbelle started squeaking from the top of the stairs. The squeaks got louder and more intense as she bounded down. I fielded her from the bottom step, held her firmly in my arms and carried her into the kitchen.

'Now look, Stinkerbelle! Look what you've been brought!' She looked, stopped squeaking with rage at having her kitchen invaded, and squeaked with excitement instead.

'I know,' I said, 'I'll put some in the big bowl and she can chase them round in there!' It was dragged into the kitchen where we ladled fish and water into it, then telling her two benefactors to stand well back in case she wanted to bite them, I let Stinkerbelle go, but she was too interested in what was splashing around in her plastic bath to worry about visitors. Standing up on her back feet, she leant over the side of the bowl watching intently.

A few seconds later and she was up, balancing on the rim. Then a sudden dive and a whoosh of water waved over the side as an otter somersaulted, circled, trapped a fish, pushed it up, over and followed it out, wetly pawing it over the floor together with a goodly slop of water. It washed over towards the cement. 'Oh, the cement!' I exclaimed. It was lifted up on to the stove. There wasn't much room to manoeuvre. One of the young men sat on the sink bench, the other stood on a chair with his head against the glass roof and almost fell

off when Jacka, the female parrot who has a decided penchant for men, flew across and sat on him. I picked her off. She made a growly sound and angrily fluffed up her feathers. Both parrots were put back into their cages.

Meanwhile, Stinkerbelle had the fish against her drinking bowl, grappling, biting, the movements almost too fast for the eye to follow as she got it between her teeth to shake and subdue it before holding it up between her paws and starting to chew from the tail end.

After a couple of mouthfuls she realized that a lot of swishing was still going on in the bowl and even more interesting was the splashing from the bucket. The maimed fish was dropped as with a bound she was in again. Fish and water flew everywhere. We all got excited and wet footed. Parrots screeched, fish were flapping under cupboards, in the dustpan, under the central heating pipes; one was covered with sand. Stinkerbelle leapt out streaming water and began pushing yet another under the fridge. Leaving that one, she trapped another, bit it, then left it for a fourth. The kitchen was full of dying fish and was beginning to look like the aftermath of a deluge.

'You can see how she loves them!' I said enthusiastically, 'but we'll have to give them to her one by one, in the bathroom perhaps,' and grabbed her. She was very wet.

We emptied water out of the bowl, then poured what was left in the bucket into that. A few more flipped out. Stinkerbelle struggled in my arms, squeaking loudly, aggressively. In the midst of narking otter, an absolute chaos of fish, flood, cement, tools and parrot screeches stood two fascinated fishermen asking questions which I tried to answer. Yes, she does tend to bite strangers, so I'm afraid you can't stroke her.

That's right, her name is Stinkerbelle-the-Nark. Nark happens to be the Thai word for otter – if you get the tone right of course. Well, I mean she *did* stink when we first got her. We rescued her from a dealer's market stall when we were living in Bangkok. She was one year old then I think; about four and a half now. Yes, she had a mate in Thailand but we let him free in a Thai National Park. Stinkerbelle wouldn't leave us though. She had other ideas about comfort, and was liable to attack and scream at strangers, especially those carrying guns, so we were rather, er, stuck with her.

No, the parrots we got when we lived in West Africa about six years ago. This is Jacka and that's Oskar. Shut up, Stinkerbelle! No, this is just a complaining noise now. Yes I do have an owl, a little owl, rather like the English Little Owl, but mine is an *Athene bramah*. We got him in Thailand too. He's upstairs at the moment, but . . .

Yes she is getting a bit aggravated, Stinkerbelle *do* be quiet!

After a time it got too much for all of us. I wished I could offer them a beer, but couldn't get to the fridge, so asked them if they'd have several on me at the pub. I thanked them again and out of the kitchen they paddled, flabbergasted at the way some people live. To make matters worse, just as they got to the gate Owlphonso, at his usual evening position on his upstairs window perch, gave one of his ear-splitting series of high screeched 'Prrps!'

Stinkerbelle was quietening down but was still excited, straining to get back to her bowl. I told her I wasn't having any, shoved her upstairs with Owlphonso and shut the door.

I realized then that the radio had been on through all this. Someone was talking about aesthetic principles in some literary work. I thought briefly of my Great-Novel-in-Progress, then turned off the radio and took stock of the kitchen floor. I'll just have to tip them out and let the poor things gasp their last in the shower, I thought. Kinder anyway than letting them be chased around and maimed. At this point, I began mopping up the flood, gingerly picking up dying or half dead, but still very flappy fish from a kitchen floor which looked like the deck of some fishing trawler awash for days and battered by a force ten nor'wester.

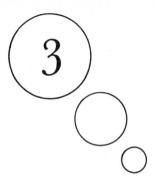

As soon as I got the kitchen organized – new shelves, sinkbench, polished quarry-tiled floor, everything neat, gleaming and in place with the sun coming in the line of back windows and filtering in through the glass roof – Stinkerbelle decided she'd take over most of it.

First she made sure that she still couldn't open the fridge and found, to my relief, she couldn't, because my husband, Forbes, before he'd had to fly off, had organized a cross-cord system over the handle, the cord being attached by screws to the sink bench.

Having given up the fridge, Stinkerbelle then dragged her foam rubber mat and positioned it nicely in front of the pot cupboard. After this, there sounded a clatter of pots and pans as she, having pushed open the sliding door, went in to investigate its possibilities. From the shelf of this cupboard she could, after some thought and determination, reach up, get her paws between the back of the knife and fork drawer, and shove it open. Having done this, she then found it quite simple to hoist herself up and round over the back of it, land amid the knives and forks and hang her whiskery face and one paw out of the front.

We considered each other thus for a while. She said 'Eeeh!' finding the forks uncomfortable and knowing she was where she ought not to be. I remembered a carving knife was sharing the drawer with her and gave in. It was too much trouble anyway to be continually attempting to stop her doing what she was determined to do. 'If you can't beat 'em, join 'em,' is a useful motto when living with otters – in fact

26

it's a necessary one if one doesn't want to end up a near nervous wreck.

The pots, pans, bucket and cleaning-up things in the under sink pot cupboard were removed and a blanket put in where the bucket once was. Knives and forks were emptied out of the drawer. Stinkerbelle waited quite patiently until this was done, then snaffled an old scarf and jersey of mine, dragged them after her through the cupboard, got them up into the drawer and twirled around with them until another cosy little bed had been made.

She liked curling up in this drawer; it was just her size. It afforded me much amusement too. Sometimes she would sleep with one paw hanging over the edge, sometimes with a bit of tail. I rather liked pulling open a drawer and finding an otter there. When I remembered, I put a large bread board with a brick on it on the bench as an over-hang to make sure she wouldn't get from the drawer to the bench.

Her dog basket, under the work-shelf and wedged between stove and wall in a dark corner, she forgot about for a while, for she liked changing her sleeping quarters. Whenever she did so, scarfs, old woollens, any clothes or newspaper I'd happened to have left within otter reach would be carried into the preferred holt, which would then be reorganized in the most comfortable fashion an otter could devise; an energetic swivelling round and round, a burrowing under, a deep sigh and finally the Nark curled up sound asleep.

In the outside garden shed she had her old travelling cage covered over with black felt and stashed with a woollen rug or perhaps bracken, bunches of which I'd bring back from the park for the purpose. Like most otters of her kind she seemed to enjoy making new holts for herself, carrying things off to stuff them with.

If I went out for more than two hours during the day I would shut the back door, leaving the dog hole open, close the glass door between kitchen and dining-room, but make sure the bathroom door was open so Stinkerbelle could get to her spraint tray. I'd also leave her the small ice-box with an appropriate amount of fish in it close to her water bowl. She became very adept at opening the lid of this and fishing out a snack whenever the mood took her. She could also fish out

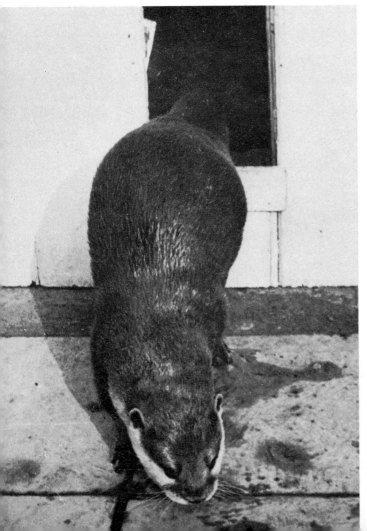

the blocks of ice which she loved to play with, batting them across the floor or swishing them around in her bowl.

She ate about fourteen ounces of food a day and sometimes more for she thought a great deal about her stomach. On an average she had ten ounces of fish – plaice, mackerel, sometimes eel – and four ounces of mincemeat. The meat was minced so that additives could be put in and one could be sure she got her vitamin intake. She liked mincemeat so much that she soon got over her displeasure concerning the additives.

She had her first snack in the early morning, another at lunch time, her third about five or six and a fourth about ten. In summer though, there might be a fifth small one, since the days were so much longer and she expended so much more energy.

I cut the plaice and mackerel into pieces after gutting them and made the mistake of cutting the fish up too small. I didn't realize at first that she, like any other animal will readily fall into bad habits especially if it means less trouble for themselves. Like humans, they are open to the corruptions of easy living. What I should have done was to give her larger cross sections instead of thinking, well, she likes small fish, so I suppose three or four-inch pieces will be all right. She got fussier and fussier about the way her food was prepared and instead of being firm, I gradually gave in, thinking she knew best. After a period when she wouldn't sniff at anything that wasn't filleted, I began to understand that if this went on she'd have me arranging her fish like a Japanese flower-styled, raw-fish dish so we went back to the usual bone-filled chunks.

She was also getting decidedly plump which didn't worry me too much as she was fit, strong, glossy, could outrun and outwalk me in the park and anyway, I thought, a little extra fat wouldn't hurt in this colder climate. But it's very easy to spoil, give in to animals and lead them into bad habits when you live in such close contact with them.

Stinkerbelle's evening snack, however, was to a large extent expended in energy during our usual after dinner tug-and-wrestle match. She would wait impatiently until I had put on my oldest jersey and the game would start with me rolling her round on her sponge mat while she tried to hold on to the skin of my hand, or grip my sleeve. After this, she dived into her pot cupboard, purposely leaving the end of her tail sticking out so that I could give it a smart thwack! Immediately she whirled round, dashed out at full speed and leapt for my sleeve.

Some very quick movement and thinking on my part, but an even faster reaction on hers and we had both worked out in that split second how my sleeve was to have her teeth gnashed into it and not my arm. Then, with her front arms and paws gripped round my wrist, I heaved her up until she stood on her back feet and tail base frantically worrying and tugging. There was power in those neck muscles and her teeth were strong. I would try to grab and hang on to the loose skin behind her neck while she twisted, pulled or rolled over and over, her teeth always firmly fixed in my loose sleeve, twisting it up until it was so tightly coiled, it wouldn't stand it any more.

I heaved her up off her back feet then, so that in mid air and hanging on by her teeth she could spin like a top, faster and faster as my sleeve uncoiled back to its original shape. She liked spinning. The game got rougher.

She was like a bouncy bit of muscular rubber and every so often she dashed back into the pot cupboard so that I could repeat the slap on her tail, the signal for her to leap out again, sometimes doing a sort of somersault to catch my sleeve. It was only fair and cricket apparently when I used one hand and arm. If I used two, she snorted and looked put out. After all, she made up the game in the first place and I was expected to keep to her rules. As for myself, I looked a bit put out when she misjudged and her teeth dented my skin. She didn't go through, but when I said 'ow!' she stopped, lay on her back for a second or two, then came over, sniffed, squeaked a little, rolled over again, and put her head on my hand making her I'm-sorry submissive whine. So I told her it was all right, slapped her on the tail, and away we went again.

Sometimes she lay curled in a semicircle and I started spinning her round, slowly at first, then faster and faster as she gained momentum.

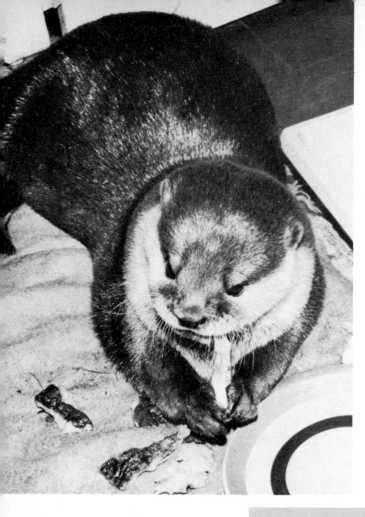

Games worked up to a point where she made excited squeaks and became a veritable yo-yo of energy: the strength in her front paws and shoulders never failed to surprise me.

When I had just about had enough and was beginning to feel somewhat dizzy and exhausted, I switched to the paper game; a rolled-up newspaper was poked in one side of the pot cupboard. She immediately rushed inside to make a grab for it. I slid open the other door a little and with her in and me out, a game of cunning wait-and-watch went on. She was very quick to learn a system: I could go from A to B twice, then I would have to go AA or BBA and so on.

When I was tired of this, I rustled paper in her drawer. At once she climbed the small shelf in the pot cupboard, got her paws behind the knife drawer and shoved it open. If I happened to be kneeling in front of the drawer at this stage, I ended up with a black eye or an almost broken nose as, without any warning, the drawer flew open and the handle landed in my face.

I hadn't time to complain though, because the Nark had already wriggled in and had her paws dangling over the open front trying to get a hairclip out of my hair as she waited for the next paper game. This consisted of sliding paper slyly along the front of the drawer while she, according to her own rules, kept her head down, tried to locate its whereabouts and fish it up with her paws only.

A hairclip and a button in the drawer next and I left her in there juggling one or the other, knowing that she would be content to amuse herself for a while. I washed my hands, inspected the dents and was surprised again how few there were and how amazing it was that she knew exactly how hard to bite even at her most boisterous without actually hurting or ever going through the skin.

And after all this, resting with my evening drink I began wondering again whether I would ever be able to concentrate again on my novel, that huge work sitting on the dining-room shelf in great forlorn heaps demanding attention. And I was still wondering about this when I heard the fridge door bang, realised I hadn't put the cord back over the handle and that Stinkerbelle was in there dragging out her bag of mincemeat and gorging herself on tomorrow's quota.

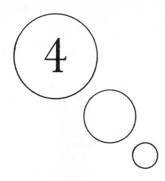

4

If it hadn't been for Stinkerbelle's presence, improvements due to the back garden would have been left to last. I personally would have preferred to have had a proper shower first, instead of one which almost wasn't. But the back garden got top priority.

After getting rid of a truckload of rubbish, I dug in a large fibreglass pool, spaded over what was to be lawn, raked it, then found that everyone had run out of turfs for the moment.

For a while, Stinkerbelle had a marvellous time grubbing away in the soil, dashing into the pool, muddying that up, rolling again, then bounding in through the back door dog-hole, leaving earthy traces everywhere. I was getting a bit short on good temper when finally the turf got laid.

Ah, now I can relax, I thought and did for five minutes because then she invented a new game – the turning-up-of-turfs game. She grubbed them up and scattered them all round the edges. All right! I said and put a line of bricks around the periphery of the fence. Fine! she thought, pushed them all to one side and began digging again.

I'll fix you! I said and went and ordered a great heap of bowling-green pebbles and York stone which duly arrived in the front garden and had to be carted through the house into the back. A thick edging of heavy, smooth bowling green pebbles went along the fence. Then a bag of cement was bought and the bricks cemented down. The rest of the pebbles were put round her pool area, York stone was set in around the edges and that was that done.

Near the back door was still a quagmire so a couple of men came and laid a nice stone terrace. I added a little brick wall (I was getting good at brick walls) up to the level of the lawn and at that point I felt satisfied. Logs went around her pool, an old rose tree hung over it and Stinkerbelle seemed to like the scene. She had lawn to play on, a largish pool to swim in, stones to delve under, logs to explore around and run on and she had the terrace for her drying mats, food tray and so on. We were, I thought, at last getting somewhere.

But to get anything done at all, a fairly strict routine had to be observed.

Owlphonso always began it; a raucous, pre-dawn prrp-prrp-cackle-hoot-shriek-shriek! jolting me upright and presumably, as the sound echoed along the line of semi-detacheds, jolting everyone else upright as well. Meanwhile, the speckled grey and white little owl calmly sat on his window perch staring out at a sky getting red and expecting an answer from one of the tawnys in the big chestnut trees across the way. 'Pish!' I said to distract his attention. He turned his head, 'Pish!' he answered, then flew over to the top rung of the loft ladder which was his eating perch.

I rolled out of bed, got his jar of fly cocoons and meal worms, picked up an old pair of tweezers, and still half asleep managed to sort some cocoons out from between wriggly, fat maggots which hadn't yet cocooned. He got a mixture of cocoons and meal-worms in his dish, then I scratched his head and held another little pishing conversation with him before sneaking back to bed. I say 'sneak' because I was determined not to wake up Stinkerbelle the Nark, wherever she might have been sleeping.

Sometimes I would get half an hour, but generally it was not so long before she woke, yawned, stretched, and if she happened to have gone to bed downstairs instead of up, swarmed out of her pot cupboard, her kitchen drawer, or the basket she was supposed to sleep in. Usually I heard the clank of her spraint tray as by this time I was sleeping fairly lightly to say the least, what with Owlphonso gliding close to my head and the room getting lighter.

So the spraint tray went clank. This was followed by a gobbly drinking sound and I waited for it. First, it was a soft queried 'Hah?' from the bottom of the stairs. I kept my eyes closed, hoping for another few seconds' sleep. 'Hah?' she said again, but worried now, so I had to say 'Hah!' back. 'Hah! *Hah!*' she responded with excitement as she came bounding up the stairs. I hurriedly submerged under sheets, blankets and pillows, but she was at the side of the bed, her paws on the edge. 'Hah yourself!' I said as she scampered around to her chair, climbed up and bounded on to my stomach which made me leap up and gave her the opportunity of burrowing down to my feet.

Leaving her in bed, I staggered down to the kitchen to let Jacka and Oskar out of their cages. They were fist-sized, green and golden-yellow with grey heads. They flew up to their perches to begin preening. I put a piece of paper in direct line with their tails and under each perch to catch the morning splop before I got Owlphonso's meat and roughage out of the fridge.

As soon as she heard the fridge door, Stinkerbelle was up and out of bed, down the stairs and round my feet. I put some fish and a fresh bowl of water in her tray and took it all upstairs again, closely followed by the expectant Nark.

Owlphonso was given his food and otter and owl were shut in together so I could breakfast in peace. While calmly drinking my tea, however, I got a nibble, first on one ear, then on the other from two parrots demanding their toast crusts. Jacka then demanded two spoonfuls of tea which had to be neither too hot, too cold, too strong or five minutes stale. If it was not to her exact liking, she would fluff up, then angrily rap her beak on the table top. Otherwise she drank it from the tilted spoon.

After breakfast I got a bag of frozen, chopped plaice out of the icebox, put it to one side to thaw, then took out a quarter of a pound of lean stewing steak. I spent some time looking for the mincer attachments and finally found the essential screw in a shoe in the pot cupboard where Stinkerbelle had been playing with it. When the meat was minced, I grated some carrot on top of it, added a teaspoon of Bemax, a quarter-teaspoon of halibut liver oil, a few drops of Abidec, one ground-up kelp tablet, one yeast tablet and one of bone meal. This

38

was mixed up, pressed together, pushed into a plastic bag and put back in the fridge.

Bird cages were cleaned and supplied with food while Oskar flew upstairs to the small back room where, perched on a chair in front of the window, he began his morning concert. Since Oskar, who was a year younger than Jacka, grew bigger than his mate and became a bully, Jacka didn't whistle much. Before Oskar started to screech and get over fond of himself, she used to whistle all sorts of tunes very nicely. She never copied these tunes from me, because I'm sure that to her intelligent ear, my whistling was too awful to mimic. She got all her nice tunes from Forbes when both of them took their morning showers. She even used to whistle part of the Senegalese national anthem.

Oskar however, *did* copy my poor attempts. I had two or three – the Blue Danube, something which might be from anywhere in Gilbert and Sullivan and something else the name of which I could never remember but had to do with some sort of angel walking up a church aisle in the midst of choir voices and had very dramatic and Victorian tragic overtones pertaining to long-lost or loved people, prison walls, angels and other assorted.

So with Oskar upstairs, mimicking an off-key flat piece of Victoriana with an embarrassing exactitude and with Jacka on my head, I started my shower, answering his whistling at the same time. Both of us cracked after every few bars and were flat all the way.

After we had gone through our repertoire, Oskar continued with tut-tutting noises, bird calls or otter squeaks until I started cleaning my teeth – the signal for him to hurriedly fly downstairs again and on to my shoulder. From this position he enjoyed trying to pick toothpaste out of my mouth, while Jacka still on my head tapped with her beak to show her disapproval and my skull began to feel quite vulnerable.

Owlphonso got the rest of his gizzard and liver when the parrots were recaged. I checked to see that his cough balls or pellets were in firm shape, then ruffled his head feathers, talked to him and gave him a length of wool to play with.

His water bowl and scratch tray were put on the table in the sun. Owlphonso liked to sun himself. Besides earth and sand, a bottle top, a cork, a couple of little pieces of wood, some string, a bit of bean, a button and some peanut husks were in the tray. Owlphonso liked to play with all these things from time to time. I noted there was a fly buzzing round which probably meant a cocoon must have fallen and hatched out between the new and still-shrinking floorboards.

It was nice though for Owlphonso to have a fly or two to catch, I thought as I managed to get an irate otter out of my bed and down to her pool where she was helped in, held under, soaked and swirled around; a rough method but the only way of making her really come to in the early morning.

After drying herself off, she felt much livelier, groomed herself, then stood up at the fridge door squeak-pipping, expecting the other half of her breakfast before our cross-country.

At about ten-thirty or so we were home again. Owlphonso had seen

us through the window where he had been keeping an eye on the odd passer-by and the parrots screeched a welcome, as they always did when they heard me open the front door.

As soon as her lead was off, Stinkerbelle dashed straight for her spraint tray in the bathroom. This particular tray was once a meat roasting pan; an aluminium square job which could be easily washed out. I didn't have to be meticulous about washing it out too thoroughly since the spraint had eaten into the metal and the smell clung.

Stinkerbelle's kind of Asian otter does seem to like to go exactly where they went before, which made life easier. Females of her kind are neater about this than the males, but English *lutra* or larger types of otter are definitely more careless about where they spraint. I was glad she was not one of those.

The tray was tilted slightly, the front end resting on sponge rubber;

the tilt was to prevent her getting her feet messy. Stinkerbelle was rather fastidious about that. She got in, sniffed, turned around and lifted her tail. A prissy, pursed-up-mouth expression came over her whiskery face. It was a high society, prim, prudish look of disapproval, the sort of look that can be seen on unamused upperclass faces. I thought of Queen Victoria. She opened her mouth, went 'Eeh!', turned round to sniff, then satisfied, left the tray.

I put some mincemeat mix in her food tray and her drying towels out on the terrace, then I pushed her outside, firmly closed the back door and left her to it.

While my lunch was cooking I read or watched the parrots because possibly they'd decide they wanted a bath. They let me know whenever they wanted a bath by swooping around in an excited way when I was in the process of washing my lettuce leaves. After a while I just *knew* they wanted a bath. So I piled the odd bits of wet lettuce leaf and some cabbage leaves on top of the dish-drying rack, removed the knife and fork drainer, put a large shallow dish of water on the bench for Jacka and let a small, steady stream of water run out of the tap for Oskar.

Bully Oskar always took his bath first. A flap and flutter into the lettuce leaves, a neat little twist around the drying rack and he was standing on the large tile which I balanced from the radiator across to the sink. This tile was tilted so the stream of water running on to it didn't go on the floor. The next thing Oskar did was try to climb up the filament of water. It broke up in his claw each time he grabbed it. He shook his head, fluffed his feathers, ran through it and galloped back again, before taking off up to the drying rack for a gambol in the lettuce. Then he hung upside down from a bar of the rack, somersaulted down to the tile again and I helped him out by giving him a sprinkle with the washing-up brush dipped in a pot of water until he was so wet that he could barely whirr up to his perch. After towel-drying him off, I settled him down on his perch under the glass roof in the sun.

Then it was Jacka's turn. Jacka, not liking the tap idea, did her usual running hop across the bench, continued through the shallow dish of water and out the other side. A flutter up to the lettuce leaves, a pause

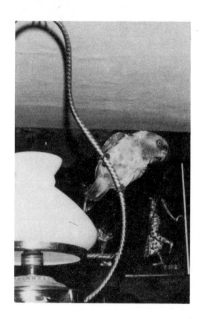

to shake and fluff, then a hop down for another run through. About five minutes later she was also dried off and two damp, bedraggled-looking birds watched me eat my lunch as they preened themselves.

For the past ten minutes Stinkerbelle had been squeaking vociferously while batting and tugging at the outside door, but with the radio on at generous volume I managed to ignore her. At such a time Wagner was found acceptable.

Most animals like to siesta for a while in the afternoons. I was no exception. In Senegal and Thailand heat, my siesta used to be taken in an air-conditioned room. In the former country, two parrots and one dog joined me. In the latter, one dog, two otters, two parrots, two owls, a civet cat and sometimes, inadvertently, a flying squirrel or two shared the comfort of a cool room.

In England it was an owl and an otter and the latter, feeling boisterous, demanded a game. Five minutes later, however, I cocooned myself in a rug and imitated her narky growl every time she tried to pull it off.

She woke up first, hauling the pillow from under my head, poking her paws in my hair searching for hairclips, bouncing on my stomach and generally carrying on with 'I want' squeaks which were about as conducive to the nerves and quiet rest as an alarm bell or a humming mosquito.

The kitchen still smelt of grilled herring. Stinkerbelle tugged at the fridge door. Balancing on my left foot, I held her away while I got the string otter-preventer off the handle. By doing some nifty footwork with my right one, I managed to get out a small snack for her before she leapt into the vegetable box. I put her outside again, together with a couple of balls and an old shoe to poke them in. After all this, I shut the dog-hole and the lower half of the stable door so she couldn't get back inside.

Before settling down to work, the parrots were let out to fly around in their glass-roofed kitchen domain. Two hours later however, Stinkerbelle was sounding so desperate to get back inside, that we shifted around to accommodate her. It would have been much easier if Jacka hadn't chased Stinkerbelle or tried to attack her everytime she saw the otter. A small jealous parrot can't do much damage to an otter, but Jacka didn't seem to realize this. She also didn't realize that Stinkerbelle could have taken off her head with one bite. Stinkerbelle however, always ran and tried to hide under her blankets when she saw Jacka coming. I was glad she had this inhibition about biting back.

When the evening was well advanced and darkness grew in the summer sky, the Nark took over the front of the house, annoying me by trying to climb on to the table, worming herself into my lap, my ink,

44

my thought, or my drink, trying to get the ice cube out so she could bat it down to the floor and into my shoe. Oskar meanwhile had taken himself back to his cage where, on his sleeping perch, he fluffed out, put his head under his wing and drew one claw up into his feathers. If disturbed once he had gone to bed, he would get so annoyed that he would make an enraged, darting lash at me with his beak and sound his fury with some growly noises from the back of his throat.

Jacka though, with Oskar out of the way, decided that now was the time she could get some undivided attention, so I put Stinkerbelle back in the kitchen with the dog-hole open to the outside and Jacka came into the dining-room, pattered around on the table and got a fair share of neck feather ruffling since she followed my pen as it moved across the page, put her head down and stood there waiting for attention.

An annoyed otter, tired of splashing about by herself and again thumping and squeaking at the dog-hole was the signal for Jacka to be put back into her cage with a walnut to chew at. The Nark bounded in as I took up fresh food to Owlphonso.

I left the front bedroom door open so he could fly down when he had eaten or had tired of watching the sky go black or prrp-cackle-shrieking at anyone walking down the street towards the pub. I ran a sponge mop over lino which had been laid over most of the bedroom carpet and went down to join the Nark in a snack, both of us stoking-up on energy before our wrestling match.

For a while then it was peaceful: Stinkerbelle, after her game, was taking a short nap and the parrots were asleep, but as soon as I started typing, Owlphonso appeared at the top of the stairs.

'Pish!' I answered back and soon the soft grey and white little owl glided silently over the table to perch on the carriage of my typewriter. His yellow eyes were open wide, staring at the movements of keys as he was carried along to the end of the run. The ping of the bell always made him jump off, fly to my head and from there to a shelf and back again for a repeat performance.

Or perhaps from his shelf he would watch a button or a pen top roll over the table. His head would swivel, then he would stretch up

45

to his full height and look down his beak at it. But soon, with a quick glide he would be in front of it, doing a funny prance-strut. After this he would stand and stare at it very solemnly for a while, move his head like a dancer's belly to get his sights right, turn away to loftily ignore it, then suddenly turn back again, stretch and with a startled look on his face, pounce. He would lift his claw, close his eyes and nibble at his catch, stretch up, stare at it again and I would get another comical, belly-dance routine before off he went, gliding away with it.

Too soon the Nark woke up and carried on around my feet, pushing paperclips between my toes, demanding another wrestling match, which she didn't get, or trying to infiltrate on to the table. When I finally went to bed she came up to bounce, wanting another game, or stubbornly trying to burrow in, while I, just as stubbornly, pushed her back on to the chair covered by a blanket at the side of the bed. Sometimes she slept in one of her holts in the kitchen which meant I had a more peaceful night.

Owlphonso prrped and bumbled in and out of his hanging basket, ate some more, shrieked once or twice, and finally we all got to sleep gathering strength for the new day in which the whole process with minor variations would be repeated, starting as usual just before dawn.

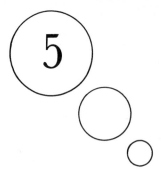

5

Of course it was only temporary, I told myself, but it's all quite ridiculous! Here I was being general maidservant to a collection of animals, yet as time went on their personalities, their needs, demanded more of my sense of responsibility, affection and indeed respect.

It would have been easier to cope if I had cut the parrots' wings, but that was something I could no longer contemplate doing. I could have taken the Nark for a long walk every second or third day perhaps, but she enjoyed her long walks and swims in the park so much, I felt they were the central point of her day. Besides, she had to have exercise. It worried me that she had no mate. I was worried too that Owlphonso wasn't getting things like mice and small birds to eat although he seemed fit and well and those smooth lacquered pellets of indigestible roughage he coughed up, as all owls do from time to time, were in firm shape.

It became important to keep the animals content for my peace of mind as well as theirs: they had to have as much free space and exercise as conditions allowed. But I wondered how long it all would go on and hoped that Forbes would soon finish all that travelling he was being subjected to. Meanwhile, just when I was typing a revised chapter of my novel and thinking how good it was to be working on it again and relishing the concentration, Stinkerbelle came on heat or on oestrus. Whatever you like to call it, it was a real bore.

It was about five weeks after the last time which wasn't so bad; the usual intense activity had gone on for only a day. This time it looked more serious. I cleaned out her pool, rehooked the hose over the old rambler rose and let the water fall in from a good height. She enjoyed playing with a stream of water like this and it kept her happy for a while. Then I put heavier stones along the bottom of the fence to stop her digging up the pebbles, excavating with her strong forepaws and continuing on to the foundations with the determination of a gang of oildrillers. I knew she couldn't get out this way but I was trying to save the shrubs, the clematis and the roses, the roots of which were protected by the bowling green pebbles – except when the Nark was on heat.

Next I saw her clambering up the two scaffolding boards put there for the express purpose of stopping her clambering up that bit. One tipped over and she found a little knot hole through which she pushed a finger, then a paw. I nailed a piece of wood over this. After that, she tried pulling down my clematis and generally leaping at the smooth pieces of ply I had put along the bottom of the woven cedar fence to stop her climbing up, which otherwise she could do easily. When she wasn't on heat, these boards were sufficient even though they were only three feet high. When she *was* on heat, they obviously weren't, so I coaxed her into the kitchen, left her there and went out to get some more lengths of ply delivered.

I called them her heat-boards. When boarded on to the fence they made a smooth vertical surface of four feet, which even in the extreme desperation to which this state led her, she couldn't possibly leap over, on to, or otherwise negotiate.

I was just putting up the last heat-board when she rushed past me, muddy from her latest lawn dig and darted into the kitchen. I took my time about chasing her because I was putting in the last nail and she couldn't get out anywhere from the house – or so I thought.

I was about to stand back and survey my handiwork, when I had a feeling. It was never wise when living with such an animal to ignore such a feeling. I made a dash for the lounge. Stinkerbelle's tail was disappearing over the window sill because I hadn't shut the window latch properly. A few seconds later, I opened the front door and tripped over an old milking stool which should have been a trendy side table, but instead was a functional toe-stubber and neck-breaker. My big toe felt as if someone, wearing hobnails, had just stamped on it. But there was no time to consider this: Frustrated Fanny was galloping up the street in the general direction of the common.

I did a very rare sort of sprint for me and began to gain on her. She heard me coming, realised she couldn't make it, stopped suddenly and rolled over submissively on her back. With a quick bit of nifty footwork I managed to stop myself landing with both feet on her stomach. My toe hurt. I picked her up, talked to her and limped back. She complained. It's not *your* toe, I told her.

Once back in the house, I offered her food but she didn't want it. For once she had more serious things on her mind; Stinkerbelle was really in a bad way. So was my toe; I took off my shoe and went about in my socks for a while. I tried playing with her but she wasn't interested. I began treating her like an invalid. 'Never mind, poor Stinkerbelle,' but she wasn't having such treatment, she was far too lively anyway. She wanted her head scratched, she wanted continual company and some grooming but she didn't want to play.

In the evening, she sat for five minutes with an orange she'd filched from the fruit bowl, rolling it around in her lap. Then she started rather desperately licking herself in frustrated regions making plaintive little squeaky noises in the process. I didn't find this very conducive to concentration on a good prose style, so I pushed away my work and told Stinkerbelle that yes, it was all very sad, but sooner or later she'd have a mate again and in the meantime she would just have to put up with it.

Two days later she was as bad as ever. On our park walks she infuriated me by insisting on going in all the opposite directions to the one in which I pointed. We walked along, with me going forward and Stinkerbelle tugging at the end of the lead and crabbing sideways. When swimming down stream, she was liable to leap off at a tangent and so unexpectedly that I had to keep a firm hold on the lead and make sure my feet weren't on any slippery banks.

She seemed to know she was being narky and every so often rolled over, made her submissive apologetic noises and dragged my hand

down to her head to have it stroked. A kind of sympathy developed, but she was not the same playful, carefree animal. I felt though that if she did for some reason evade me in the park, she would go off on her own, searching for a suitable spouse. This meant I had to take extra precautions to keep her close and under strict observation.

On the third day she hid behind the fireplace stove in the lounge and when I went looking for her in the kitchen, she managed, by using all her strength, to pull the new draught cover off the bottom of the front door. I left it off. We were going out for a walk anyway. I put the usual things in the bike basket and went back to get my otter coat, thinking she had gone into the kitchen.

She hadn't – as a call from two cottages down testified. There she was in Miss Hewett's garden, dabbling around in her bird bath. 'I thought there couldn't be *two* of them round here!' said Miss Hewett. 'I just looked out of my window and she bounded into the garden ever so quickly!' I thanked her for calling me and picked up Stinkerbelle. She complained bitterly.

On the fourth day I worked out a system of cross checks on all possible escape routes, then leaving her I bicycled down to the shops to buy her an eel. 'Please kill it properly,' I said, 'and chop it up.'

'Wot? Chop it up, luv?'

'That's right, chop it and I'll have three plaice and one mackerel as well and I'll be back in ten minutes.'

Then I bought Stinkerbelle's meat and one chop. After which I bought bread, groceries, greens, bird seed, maggots and returned to the fish shop.

'Seen you somewhere before, haven't I?'

'And I'll have a trout,' I said hungrily.

'Want it chopped up too, do you?'

'No, thank you, it's for me. Leave its head on though.'

'Better half likes em jellied, eh?'

'Eh?'

'Eels.'

'No, raw.'

'Wot? Oh well, never mind, it takes all sorts, don't it?'

'It's for strength and vitality actually,' I said.

'Well, well! Have a good time now, luv.'

When I got home, Stinkerbelle was waiting for me. I unpacked the fish; she got parsley with her eel. The eel hadn't quite been chopped through : each individual piece wriggled. The Nark stood up on her back legs and squeaked excitedly. I gave her the tail first since it was the bit that was wriggling the most. She tucked it under one arm and lopped over to the water bowl where she sloshed it round, chased it, caught it, and after all this started eating it from the meaty end. She looked happier. I left her to it and hobbled out to get the rest of the provisions from the bicycle basket. My toe was still hurting.

Mrs Howard, my neighbour, was cleaning the brass on her front door.

'I can't stand much more of this!' I told her.

'Poor Stinkerbelle,' she said.

'I can hardly get my shoe on,' I groaned.

'Oh the poor little thing!'

Mrs Howard is one of those people who have a special love for and feeling for animals. She engages their immediate sympathy and animals respond to her kindness with very little reservation. She was able to pet, play with, pick up and otherwise handle Stinkerbelle, and was the only other person who was ever able to do this apart from myself, Forbes and Chalat, our motherly and friendly cook in Thailand. I was incredibly lucky to have such a helpful and neighbourly animal-lover living next door. She was fond of talking to the parrots and having whistling matches with them when they were outside. She adored Owlphonso and was always intrigued by Stinkerbelle and her goings-on.

At first, she spent some time having chats with Stinkerbelle over the fence and watching her swim, then after a while, having decided Stinkerbelle knew her well enough, she began stroking her when I brought her out of my front door and tipped her into the bicycle basket in preparation for our morning walks.

Stinkerbelle got used to these little patting, chatting sessions in the mornings. She would stand up in her bike basket, put her paws on the

53

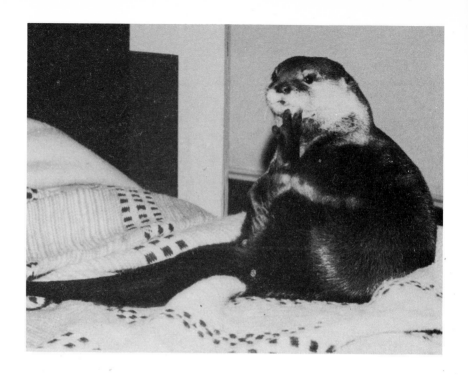

fence and wait for her enthusiastic fan to come out to admire and flatter her. She also allowed Mrs Howard to visit us, accepting her presence at once. Knowing Stinkerbelle's reputation as far as people in her house and garden were concerned and knowing her attack shrieks and biting bouts, this astounded me at first and I was rather apprehensive, but thinking of Mrs Howard's genuine affection for the Nark, perhaps it was not surprising. 'They know, these little animals *know*,' was one of her themes.

Stinkerbelle also got on well with Mrs Howard's little dachshund Buster, a sympathetic middle-aged dog with those very expressive eyes dachshunds have. When they first met, Buster was somewhat suspicious of her, since she bowled into his house on the end of a lead as if she owned it, straining to explore every nook and cranny of the new room, ignoring Buster completely. He got excited, then solemn-eyed as he watched her sniff at and into everything with her usual pushy aplomb. Later though, he worked up enough courage to sniff at her. She took time off to give him a long, slow stare over her shoulder, then while she fished for anything she could find under a chair he tentatively nudged her rump. Like any lady who's just had her bottom pinched she indignantly leapt around to face him, but he had already turned his back on her, and to show his good intentions, sat there, his hind quarters shivering as she sniffed him all over.

Soon they were getting along well. He delighted in playing with her, proudly showing off his ability to catch balls or chase after sticks until, one day in the park, he splashed in front of her while she was swimming up the water course. She gave a short, shrill scream of rage and made as if to nip him on the rump. It was a token bite, but Buster never forgave her. He got out, shook himself and sadly waddled away from the stream, aggrieved and hurt, refusing to accompany us further. He would never play with her again and whenever they met he would treat her to a sorrowful stare and quite rightly refuse to have anything further to do with such a narky creature.

But now Mrs Howard was commiserating with my problems and offering any help and advice she could give, when I said, 'If only I knew I could get her to Barbados or wherever we're going to be for a while when Forbes stops travelling, I'd get her a mate at once.'

'If I were ten years younger,' Mrs Howard replied, 'I'd take her over and keep her for you until you got back. But perhaps you could ring up some zoos. You never know, someone might have a male they don't want, or can't find a mate for.'

'A good idea!' I said. 'Yes, perhaps . . . Good God, my trout!'

I dashed back through the lounge and dining-room to the kitchen where already, through the glass door, I could see Stinkerbelle on the bench, chomping through my trout. She stopped, lifted her head. We stared at each other silently. My toe still hurt. Then she whined, knowing she was doing something wrong. I still had my chop but I exploded, 'If there's one thing I can do without,' I told her as I swung her off the bench and down to the floor, 'If there's one thing I can do without, it's a *nark on heat!*'

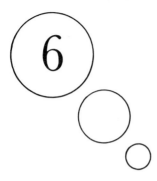

6

It still hurt to wear a shoe on my right foot, but at least Stinkerbelle was back to normal. On the evening of the fourth day when she was not on heat any more I started telephoning. I began with a call to the Caribbean and caught Forbes between island hops. After the usual preliminaries, we spent about ten pounds discussing the problem. 'Even if they agreed to have her on the island, we shouldn't consider it without a mate for her. You'll have to ask them about *two* otters. Try to persuade them,' I insisted.

'I'll do my best, but I have to go off to Guyana next, then Venezuela and . . . If you could find her a temporary home over there and with a mate, that'd be marvellous!'

'There are problems,' I said, 'But I'll try.'

So after a while I opened the zoo list and picked up the telephone. One zoo had a male, but had just got a female; another had a three-female surplus; one had two, but they didn't know quite what sex, and yet another couldn't take any animal that had been a pet. I put down the receiver thoughtfully.

Stinkerbelle was used to home comforts. Animals get used to a comfortable life in the same way as humans do. If you're accustomed to a luxurious bathroom, then it's hard to put up with a tinny wash bowl. If you're used to being pampered and waited on and haute cuisine, you're not going to like it much if you're ignored and treated as some lesser being of the lower orders.

I don't know of any being, animal, human or bird that doesn't like and appreciate a degree of comfort. No one likes to be too hot, too cold, hungry, ignored, shut in, isolated or bored. On the other hand however, if she had a mate and really good natural conditions, nice warm sleeping quarters, good food and swimming facilities, why, what more could she want?

Another problem then presented itself; would she accept a strange keeper? The day before she had attack screamed through the glass kitchen door at the milkman who stood yards away at the front. Definitely there were problems. Yet perhaps somebody would be interested enough to look after her with a mate and with the possibility of seeing her with cubs later on. I picked up the telephone again.

I talked to a person who had only Canadian otters; to a very rich man who couldn't just then because he had gorillas in his nursery; to a wild life enthusiast who might have been interested but was going away for a year. Another person knew of someone who'd *had* a male but he'd gone abroad and they didn't know what had become of the otter. After that, an Otter Authority promised to call me back if she heard anything.

Then I talked to someone who had four amblonyx, Stinkerbelle's type of otter. I held my breath. Sex? One female, one male and two female cubs, but a kind invitation to take Stinkerbelle up to visit them. Not many people invite you to bring your otter along.

So I put down the phone and went back to the terrace where Stinkerbelle was lying on her mat juggling with a plastic bottle top. It was balanced on her nose, held between her paws, dropped into her mouth and immediately was juggled back into her paws again. Then she reached her paws up and back over her head, still holding the light plastic between them. By dint of stretching her paws back and twisting she managed to land it in a shoe, whereupon she started trying to fish it out from her flat-on-her-back position and without really looking at it. Her whiskers shone in the sunlight.

'Well Stinkerbelle,' I said, digging her in the ribs, 'at least you've been invited to meet your own kind, and let's hope you behave yourself!'

Actually since her heat she had been exceptionally nice; charming in fact, responding to all commands with a commendable alacrity. When

I think about it though, I realize that it had taken about three months of living in close contact with her to get to this stage. It was a relationship which allowed us to tolerate each other's occasional snarkiness. We had developed a kind of tacit respect for one another's shortcomings and both of us had learnt to control our tempers, sometimes under trying conditions.

To a certain extent I dominated her; she accepted my authority, let herself be picked up, put anywhere, got out of anywhere, have her lead on whenever I wanted to put it on, (although five months before this was not the case) and generally accepted my orders. On the other hand, I fed her, played with her, provided her with amusement and in general acted as her general maid. But most important of all, she had not lost her stubbornness, her wilfulness, her independence. If we enjoyed each other's company and found contentment in it and if often

she was affectionate and wanting affection, there was still that quality of independence. I conceded as much as possible to her own laws and needs and in return she put an implicit trust in me and gave in to my demands as much as her nature would allow. But with no other person would she tolerate such an understanding.

Once I stretched her out on the table and with a needle dug out an offending chestnut prickle and she lay quite still, though the process of getting the prickle out caused her some pain.

We also developed a non-verbal communication. Strange this, knowing when an animal is sensing feelings and responding to them and being able to recognise emotions in the animal itself. One begins to have intimations of some sense, to a large extent smothered by civilizing processes, codes of politeness and so on. It is so non-verbal that it's almost impossible to explain, using words. It's not really a form of telepathy either, rather a finer degree of an immediate awareness of one's own sensibilities and reactions to another's and vice versa. I found that this more sensitive awareness affected my relationships with all animals, and most people, and often I wished I could ignore it. I felt that if it developed any further I would begin to sniff the air when meeting people instead of going through the usual 'How do you dos'.

But for all this Stinkerbelle would respond to even quietly conversational demands, such as 'Do get out of that flowerpot Stinkerbelle!' or, 'Get your foot *out* of the fridge please.' Or 'No, I'm not plodding through that bog again.' She still maintained her measure of independence and wilfulness however and we tacitly compromised in many a situation.

The only thing we seemed to have absolutely no agreement or communication or understanding about was her aggressiveness towards strangers. At various times we had tried roaring at her, slapping her across the nose, angrily telling her off and with practically always the same result: she would roll over on her back with her paws up, wriggle around, groan and put on a performance of simply awful submissiveness.

So you would scold her and leave her, whereupon she would look sour for a while, beg for reassurance and five minutes later she'd be

59

absorbed in a game, carrying on as if nothing had happened. One certainly can't punish an otter by beating it, for apart from the fact that it's something I couldn't do to any animal anyway, one feels that in the last resort one would turn it into a suspicious thing, surly, or ready to fight to the death.

I felt that she was bewildered and confused by a harsh scolding after she had bitten someone. It seemed beyond her comprehension. Perhaps the biting of strangers was meant to keep her clan (me) free from outside interference, protecting our relationship, but this was no doubt only a small part of the reason. The fact that Stinkerbelle had no fear of humans, that she knew she could bite and have an effect, aggravated the problem. It shamed me into realizing that too much contact with humans had led to this.

It seems to be a generally held opinion that all mustelidae, the family to which she belonged and which includes badgers, ferrets, stoats and polecats, explode into attack with a special kind of stubborn determination. The way in which badgers battle and stoats kill is well known. Nature itself seems to have afforded this special, explosive emotion which engages their whole being in the onslaught. But in natural conditions there are other outlets for aggressiveness, the continual hunting of prey, defence of territorial rights, self-defence and so forth. In conditions where these things are to a large extent repressed, there is bound to be a strain on the animal. Of course Stinkerbelle the Nark refused to let any human intimidate her and I was thankful that she hadn't the large teeth of a *lutra* otter.

The Otter Authority rang up again. She sounded very knowledgeable on the phone, helpful too. Hope loomed on the horizon. I awaited her visit with some impatience and told Stinkerbelle she'd better behave herself for heaven's sake!

The previous week I just saved the man who came to read the electricity meter from a nip on his ankle. Fortunately he didn't realize the Nark was leaping out to get at him, all bristly whiskers, flat ears and sharp teeth, so he thought she was a lovely little thing, lying there groaning and squirming in my arms which were holding her like a carpenter's vice.

60

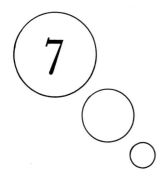

I hoped Stinkerbelle was going to be delightfully playful, all sweet insouciance and bouncily amusing. No, that was too much: I just hoped she wouldn't insolently attack scream through the glass door.

The Otter Authority was due at any minute.

I had already planned a campaign. The Nark would be put up-stairs in the bedroom some time before the arrival. She would be well fed and played with, then hopefully she would go to sleep in my bed. When the Otter Authority arrived, all should be quiet. At the door I would say, 'Sshh,' lead her quietly into the front room and sit her down saying 'Sshh, ssh!' again. I realized of course that this in itself might make an odd impression so I decided to whisper, 'Territory', which might do, temporarily. Then I'd shut the door leading from the front room into the dining-room – this door had glass panels at the top so that the O.A. would see Stinkerbelle come down the stairs, go into the kitchen and make straight for her tray in the bathroom.

While she was sprainting, I'd close the glass door between the kitchen and dining-room, then when I was giving the Nark something to eat, the O.A. could quietly open the dining-room door, stealthily get round the dining-room table, sit on it and watch the Nark through the little window, concealing herself behind the curtain. The Nark, not realizing anyone else was in her house would finish her food, maybe want a game and carry on normally. Perhaps this plan would create a good impression?

A big car drew up in front of the cottage. The Otter Authority got

out. She was on crutches. I opened the door. 'Sshh!' I said. 'Hello!' she said. She had a rather loud voice and was unexpectedly young and blonde. 'Ssh!' I said pointing up at the ceiling. 'Oh,' she said loudly. 'Sorry about the crutches, but I've just had an operation on my knee.' I whispered to her to have a seat.

'But where's the otter?' she asked.

'Well, I thought you might watch her through the glass here,' and went on to explain the position, still in a whisper. 'You see, she does bite strangers. I mean, if you could be *very* quiet, she'll be more her er – normal self . . . ' and stopped, hearing the patter of otter feet on the ceiling above. 'She's awake now so I'll . . . ' and I was about to close the Otter Authority in the front room when she followed me into the dining-room, looked up the stairs to the closed door at the top and gave a superb rendering of an otter greeting, only with a P-EW! at the front, a noise Stinkerbelle didn't usually make unless she was extremely startled or over-excited.

The reaction was immediate : a snort, a thump against the door, then a series of indignant squeaks and sharp shrieks.

'Well, er, if you'd like to wait in the front room,' I said through the din, 'I'll bring her down to the kitchen. Then when she's eating if you er – want to come in quietly, you can watch her through the glass door or the window without being seen.'

I went up, opened the door and grabbed the highly excited and suspicious Nark before she could belt on down past me, carried her into the kitchen and firmly closed the glass door.

Stinkerbelle sniffed, then looked at me as if to ask, What on earth do you think you're playing at? But nature calling, she let the situation be for the moment. I got her food, clean water and had just put it down in the usual place in front of the back door when the dining-room door opened. In the kitchen, Stinkerbelle froze for but a second before standing up on her back legs and staring through the glass kitchen door. She squeaked inquiringly, watched the stranger approach the glass, squeaked sharply, saw the stranger get nearer and gave a scream of rage.

The Otter Authority greeted her again. Stinkerbelle flung herself against the glass panel. The O.A., who was also a zoologist, crouched down to study her more closely, waggling a finger at her through the glass. Stinkerbelle got demented: the high, whining attack scream now.

'For God's sake, behave yourself!' I said. She didn't. I was still in the kitchen so I opened the back door and put her food out in the patio through the open top half: a very convenient system as it meant I didn't have to do a running dash to get in through the door before she beat me to it. I simply lifted her up and passed her over the bottom half of the stable door.

While Stinkerbelle fumed outside, the Otter Authority and I had a nice conversation about otters. She was very interesting on the subject and I kept wishing Stinkerbelle would shut up.

'Let her come in!' she said suddenly.

'Eh?' I said, then 'Er, well, she is bad with strangers. She *does* bite people. The lady next door is an exception, but she got to know her first,' I added hastily, 'so I don't know . . . She's rather excited still.'

'Bring her in!' she said.

'Well, if she's talked to, she *might* be all right. She understands the word '*my!*' said very sharply. She used to respond to this because our cook in Thailand used to say it. It means, No, don't! in Thai. And if you keep talking to her then it could work but . . . '

'Bring her in,' she said.

So I went out, picked up the Nark and prayed. Besides praying, I talked to her soothingly and fairly sternly as I carried her into the front room.

The O.A. was sitting down in a fairly low chair, her crutches on each side and her legs stretched out front.

'I don't think I'd better really, she feels too excited.'

'Put her down!' she said.

'Well if you can keep *talking* to her . . . '

'Let her come,' she said bravely.

I put the Nark down.

She scooted around the gammy leg and I breathed a deep sigh of relief for I didn't like it at all. The O.A.'s hands were held down in front of the chair for Stinkerbelle to sniff at. She sniffed. I kept up a stream of stupid chat trying to put reassurance in my voice. 'That's right, Stinkerbelle, good little otter!' and other such trivia which is embarrassing in front of a professional zoologist and Authority, but it's not *what* you say, it's the tone that counts and I was hoping that it would stop Stinkerbelle from doing her worst. And I said '*my!*' firmly and sharply here and there to warn her off.

The Otter Authority didn't talk. She was absolutely silent, motionless. They studied each other. Stinkerbelle had sniffed all over the hands hanging down in front of her nose. For a moment it seemed she couldn't make it out; the silence, the stillness, the hands presented to her. She stopped squeaking and was silent too, sniffing again. In the next instant, I realized she was no longer sniffing, but biting.

I yelled at her, grabbed her, put her back into the garden and came back shame-faced and apologetic. For a second I hadn't known she was actually biting, she had made no attack noises.

'That's all right,' the Otter Authority said, 'I've been bitten by many otters in my time.'

'What?'

'I'm used to it.'

'Oh!'

'I didn't want to yell, because I didn't want her to realize what she was doing, or that I was affected by her biting me.'

She was exceedingly brave. There was some blood on the carpet. There were three bites on the palm of the hand, paired punctures, evenly spaced. 'The sewing machine type,' the O.A. told me.

'I'll get a bowl of hot water and some sticking plaster,' I said, 'I'm desperately sorry.'

The bites were bathed and plastered. I felt even worse when I realized that that hand had to be used on the crutches. I was full of admiration at the Otter Authority's calmness and shame at Stinkerbelle's bloody-mindedness. 'Could I invite you to lunch in the pub a few doors down?' I said.

I opened the dog-hole so Stinkerbelle could get back to her own quarters in the kitchen and we went off for lunch.

The pub was crowded but as soon as the O.A. appeared people

parted and seats were given up. We settled down to a steak and kidney pie and she took out a notebook to write up recent events. I wondered what she was writing.

'She can be so . . . I mean she generally is so . . . ' I tried, 'It's just with people she doesn't know, you see.'

We talked some more about otters. She told me about whisker variation and paw-play position, about otter types, about many harassing encounters and a *lutra* which had once bitten and clawed her until her hands and arms were all bloody. I was very impressed and offered her more beer.

When we went back, Stinkerbelle began attack screaming again. Soon after, the O.A. left, promising kindly to do all she could to help me find a suitable, if temporary, home for the Nark.

After she'd gone, Stinkerbelle came out to sniff everywhere she had been standing or sitting while I told her that as far as the otter world was concerned, her reputation was zero and mine no doubt worse. And it was her own crunchy little fault – well, almost. But why couldn't she be *pleasant* to people, for goodness sake!

All in all, I was disgusted at her behaviour and annoyed with myself for trusting her too far with a stranger even if she *was* an Authority. And for a moment, I refused to rescue her from one small and jealous parrot who had her cornered in the pot cupboard.

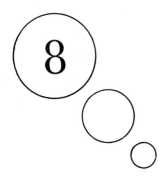

8

Jacka's jealousy of Stinkerbelle began quite suddenly and never stopped. Before it happened I could leave Stinkerbelle and parrots together without worrying about consequences. The birds would watch with interest the otter's activities and when, as happened occasionally they found themselves on the same level – i.e. the floor – there would be a beak to whisker confrontation, during which Jacka would fluff up, open her beak, make growly noises in her throat and back away before taking off.

If Oskar met Stinkerbelle, he would look quite dumbfounded; his feathers would go smooth and flat (a sign of fright), and he seemed to have no idea what he ought to do next. After a bit of troubled thought, he'd side-step out of the way before he too flew off. Stinker-belle, faced with Oskar in this state, would flatten on the floor, put her face down, slide one paw forward, then slide-hump herself a bit closer to give the bird a whiskery sniff just as Oskar turned away.

When Jacka made aggressive noises and gestures however, Stinker-belle would quickly back off. Sometimes, when she met the parrots on a bed head, or on a chair back, she'd get rather bouncy and make little mischievous feints, wanting to tease or play with them. But she always responded to a sharp warning 'No!' Stinkerbelle rarely met aggression in other animals but when she did, no matter how small the animal, she would retreat. I'm not sure whether it was because of my warning she learned to leave the parrots alone, or whether this was part of her character.

Later, when other otters decided she was not all they desired and showed it, she got very submissive and shivery. When two small Jack Russell terriers refused to be frightened off by her attack noises in the park one day, she got between my feet for protection. And when Jacka really began attacking her, she would rush into the pot cupboard and try to bury herself in her blankets.

But if my warnings of 'Stinkerbelle, *leave!*' and '*no!*' were successful, my exhortations to the bird were in vain. 'Jacka *stop* it! Look *out!* You'll get your head bitten off!' and so on, in warning or angry tone did nothing to prevent Jacka from carrying on with her attack. She had, by some bird-brained deviation come to the conclusion that Stinkerbelle was, A, attackable and B, that Stinkerbelle was taking up time which otherwise might have been devoted to her.

Apart from the jealousy though, there was probably something of the office-boss kicks office-clerk who kicks office-boy displacement aggression about it. Oskar bullied Jacka whenever he could and felt like it and she had no one to pass his bullying on to, until she discovered that she could, with some effect, chase Stinkerbelle. So there would be this small green and yellow bundle of fury flying down to make a frontal or rear attack while Stinkerbelle was innocently playing, or rather more vulnerably positioned in her spraint tray. There would be a scat of otter into the pot cupboard or dog basket, a rummage and dive under blankets while Jacka, fluffed up and enraged, pecked furiously into the hump of otter under the covers.

Sometimes Stinkerbelle wouldn't make it under her rugs in time and there she would be, squashed up on her back, her paws raised and a baffled look on her face, which had by then compacted into the folds of her loose neck skin. She never attempted to retaliate, although I presume that had Jacka dashed into her face or really managed to peck out a piece, an instinct of self-preservation would have overcome Stinkerbelle's apparent cowardice – or was it tolerance? In such a case, Jacka might have been halved at a single bite.

Not only did Jacka attack Stinkerbelle whenever she saw her, she searched for her. Even when Stinkerbelle was not in the kitchen and when the birds were free, Jacka would fly down to the pot cup-

board, growling in the back of her throat, make a thorough examination, then fly up to the knife and fork drawer, peck at that and bang her beak on the sink bench. After this she would inspect the dog basket and the bathroom. Only after she was quite satisfied that no Nark was in the area would she settle down to her own activities. In consequence, the parrots and otter could never be together without my being there to act as a strict and watchful referee.

After one such harrowing episode and having left the parrots in the kitchen, Jacka tapping her beak against the glass door at Stinkerbelle's whiskery face peeping through from the other side, I told them all that the trouble was, we shouldn't have been here at all! Jacka and Oskar should have been free-flying with hordes of their own kind above some West African baobab, or some open savannah country.

69

Stinkerbelle should have been swimming with a clan in some Thai stream and Owlphonso, swinging to and fro on the brass hanging lamp, should have been winging through an Asian night on the look out for moths and mice, and he would have been too if his beak hadn't been damaged by Oskar before we left Thailand. Not to mention me of course, who ought to have been doing all sorts of other things. And if we were not careful, I said morosely, we would all end up a bit twisted. I, at least, could envisage myself going up the wall with the responsibility, the attachment and the worry about what was going to happen to them all.

It is all very well to rescue animals from markets and dealers : there are people who do commit real crimes in capturing animals, taking them away from their true environments and treating them with an astounding lack of humanity. But maybe it's just as much of a crime to tame, to have too much contact with, to allow animals to become so dependent on you that they'll never be able to enjoy a wild life again. Animals quickly become accustomed to expect not only food, but games, interests, communication and affection.

Living too close, you become as much theirs as they yours. And as the affection you develop for them and their individual personalities grow, so does your responsibility towards them increase and at this point you realize that if you *do* leave them, they must be housed in optimum conditions and under the care of a person who is genuinely concerned for their welfare; in a word, someone who will treat them as beings and not just as mere animals – to be booted about.

'And for heaven's sake, Stinkerbelle!' I said, 'If you *must* make a nest under the table, use some newspaper and *not* my manuscript. Here!' But as I went off to make some tea I was followed by the Nark who, forgetting her nest-building and remembering her stomach, hoped to beat me into the fridge.

When I opened the kitchen door to let in the night air and push Stinkerbelle out for a swim, I noticed a decided nip in the evening air : autumn was coming in, and the moon looked cold.

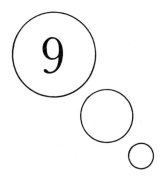

9

Since the Otter Authority's visit, I decided I was not being scientific enough about Stinkerbelle's behaviour.

Had I ever really noticed what position she put her paws in to bat, paw, pat, spat, eat or whatever else she wanted to do with them? I knew what most of her sounds meant, but did I know how many of them there were? Or for that matter, did I know which teeth were what and how many whiskers she had and where, and hundreds of details which I can't describe offhand because, like anything you live with long enough, you tend to take the whole thing for granted.

I stared at her front paws scientifically as she lay on her back juggling with a button. Sensitive stubby 'fingers' webbed on down from nail base level. Soft pads swelled under the 'fingers' and the 'palms'. The two side fingers were smaller than the three middle; same relation in length to ours in fact. The back paws, also webbed, were larger, more spread out, stronger but not so handy. The front fingernails never got to the overhanging stage, whereas the back ones sometimes did, curling over uselessly, which meant she should have been doing some more digging. When I cut off such a curled bit she complained. Stinkerbelle didn't like having her toenails cut.

I was going to study her back paws more closely but she climbed up into the kitchen drawer, reclining there with her head hanging over the front edge, watching to see what I'd get up to next. This was a fine time to study the whisker situation! How many whiskers? I counted to ten before she got so impatient that I had to tip her out and have a game with her, trying to count at the same time. I reached forty, before she realized my mind was not on the game and dashed back into her drawer. I lifted her out again. She was decidedly vexed, but she didn't know just how determined science can be.

Where the whiskers sprouted from the lighter grey parts there were little black spots. And whiskers she didn't lack : a big bunch on either side of her nose, then two other bunches spreading across the top lip, curving out and down across yet another batch just below the corners of her mouth. The latter bristled out front before curving down.

Another smaller bunch sprouted under her chin in the white patch there and she sported a small collection just further down on the greyer bit; these were very long and followed the line of her neck. She had three or four long antennae whiskers over each eye and a few shorter more bristly ones at the bend of each 'elbow'. I got to twenty-five in a side-of-nose count and gave up : boring actually. The Nark thought so too and I had to give her an extra bit of fish because by this time she was at the fridge-thumping stage.

Charlie Brown, her mate in Bangkok, had much longer whiskery whiskers than Stinkerbelle. I never knew how many. Anyway, he wouldn't have let me study them too closely. They were *his* whiskers and no one would have been able to muck about with them.

It was amazing what I found out when I began studying : all sorts of useless information cropped up and I got quite absorbed for a while. The slightly pixie shape at the tops of the small ears which I'd always considered round before; the fact that they were silvery-grey rimmed and darker inside. The slight clefting in the upper lip area. The way that pale greyish-white colour extended from under the nose, across and under the eye in a line to ear base, then along the jaw to the neck area and down the chest. Then came the real whiteness of that small under-chin patch set in the light grey.

And her teeth on each side top and bottom; the couple of big, flat-topped, grinding molars at the back, the three more pointed pre-molars, the big canine fangs – shorter lower one and longer more cur-ved upper. The row of five little incisors between the paired canines. When Stinkerbelle yawned you got a good eyeful of her teeth. The

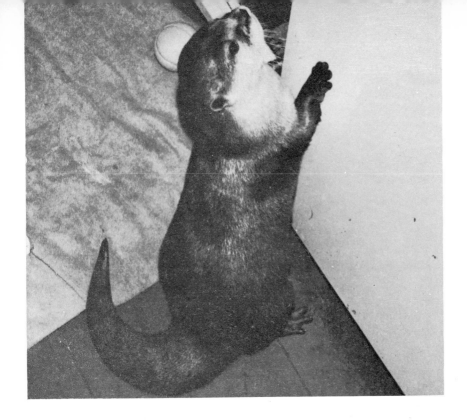

canines grabbed food and ripped it up, the premolars helped, the incisors kept the grip and did close grooming, the molars were good grinding surfaces. Looking at her teeth you could see she was no relation to a rodent even though she could resemble a beaver. Like badgers, ferrets, polecats and so on she was a true mustelidae.

Then I got out my tape measure and found her tail was $11\frac{1}{2}$ inches from base to tip, 7 inches around its base, and $1\frac{1}{4}$ just before its tip – but it was difficult to be exact when she was trying to wrestle with me and grab the tape measure at the same time. Added to this, her tail was flat underneath and it was difficult to keep the tape measure smoothly round it.

From nose to tail base she measured $19\frac{1}{2}$ inches which made her 31 inches overall. Chest measurement was 13 inches. Stomach region was 16 inches.

When I got to the stage of discovering she was $2\frac{1}{2}$ inches between her eyes and some of her whiskers were 2 inches long I began to wonder what on *earth* I was up to so I hurriedly got on to some nark noises.

I had an old meat mincer that squeaked when I turned the handle. When I was doing some bush carpentry and rather awkwardly using a brace and bit for making screw holes, this made a peculiar squeaking noise too. My bicycle wheel, rubbing against the guard, made a similar sort of squeak until I fixed it. To all these noises Stinkerbelle responded with excitement, squeaking back and trying to climb up my legs to see where the sound was coming from, because this sound was very like one of her most common ones.

These squeaks varied in expression, intensity and length depending on whether she was determinedly trying to beat my foot into the fridge = loud and determined; wanting food = demanding; when a piece of fish was descending towards her = loud and excited, then toning down to sharp little squeak-chirps as she got her paws on it.

Another variation of the sound occurred when, for instance, she was in the park and heard something unfamiliar or saw something moving in the distance; then it was head up, sniff, squeak-squeak, with query and slight alarm in it. There was a bird-like chirp to these short series of squeaks too, especially the more plaintive ones denoting 'I want to go on!' She made louder, shorter ones when she began getting aggressive, but was not yet full of sound and fury. And another variation on this squeak, rather sharper and of a seemingly higher frequency, was the sound of two otters at night, contacting or locating each other.

In the same way that the Thai language is tonal so that one word may have several different meanings depending on how it is said, so this little Thai otter's squeak could change its meaning depending on the tone, sharpness, intensity, frequency and expression used.

There was also a deeper sound she made; not a squeaky sound at all, but a deep groaning one, rather like a lamb going 'eeeh' instead of 'baah' if you can imagine it. I seldom heard her make this noise when she was with another otter and it happened only when she was lying in a state of dejected submission in front of an aggressive type. How-

74

ever, it was a sound she used frequently with me, and often she used it with growly overtones: when I picked her up, when I shoved her out of bed, when I carried her over to the pool to give her an early wake up dunking, when she had had a telling off and rolled on her back (without the growl in it here) and became submissive, or when she was generally peeved off but not in a fighting mood.

When she was up in arms though, this sound went into a much deeper, growly, shorter series of 'eerh-eerh' and when she was really browned off it came in waves of sound until the point where she made one louder, shorter, sharper '*errh!*' and demonstrated a token bite. She used to do this whenever I put on her harness. But she was still in control of herself and the bite was calculated to fall short: a gesture, not real attack.

When she *did* lose her temper, it sounded quite different. At the fridge door, bouncing around trying to get in, squeak-squeak-squeak! *eerh!* high-pitched, then *EERH!* bite. It was still not a real bite, nor had she really got me, her teeth stopping just short, but it was too close to be just a warning so I would lose my temper and turn on her, 'Stinkerbelle you *ruddy little nark!*' And over on her back she used to roll with submissive groans.

When she had her food however and I put my hand near, she would go on eating but emit at the same time a small, sinister whine. If I then attempted to take the piece there would have been a short snarly squeak ending in a *EERH!* as she lunged for my hand. With any other otter I wouldn't, of course, have dared to touch food once it had been put down. There was always a slight instinctive tension on both our parts when I had to. For instance, there was the time she stole a whole bagful of her food out of the fridge and scattered it over the floor in front of her: a tension as she ate, whining a little menacingly, keeping her eye on my hands as I gathered up the bits. The only time her mate Charlie bit me was when I picked up a couple of peanuts he had his eye on.

When Stinkerbelle dragged my roast of weekend-beef out of the fridge and on to the lawn, muddied it up and began chewing into it, I was so enraged that without more ado I stomped over, called her this and that, dragged it out of her paws, picked it up and stomped back with it, still telling her what I thought of her. Perhaps because I'd really lost my temper, Stinkerbelle, in this instance, controlled hers or got intimidated.

When otters are together, they warn each other off food they consider to be theirs. It seemed to me, when watching them, that according to their code it belongs to you if you've got your paw on it or have it in the circle of your forearms, even though you're eating another bit at the same time. If by chance there's one fish and two otters, the quickest wins, ownership is established and rarely questioned.

There was another kind of vocalization too: When she was very excited in the middle of a really tough wrestling game, which verged on the too-rough, she would make a snorty and explosive sound, not a down-the-nose or back-of-throat sound, but rather as if you're trying to clear a particularly horrible smell out of your mouth as you wrinkle up your nose, pull a face and cough at the same time. This noise – but more spitty and explosive – came when she was suddenly alarmed and it seemed to come as involuntarily as a leap back.

This happened when I was given a deer-skin rug and unpacked it in front of her. She sniffed it and leapt back with a real snort, approached it warily with short squeaky noises, then snorted back again when I moved it. She also said 'Hah!' to it appeasingly and very softly a couple of times. It took her months to get used to that deer skin and she never did feel sure about its presence, always treating it warily.

There was also an explosive 'Pew!' sound which often preceded the 'Hah!' noise and this denoted excitement crossed with some alarm, perhaps at hearing another strange otter unexpectedly near. The noise approximated a very forcibly said 'phew!', high-pitched but without the H. '*P-ew!*' then the '*hah!*'

The real sound of rage and fury however was very memorable. This was the attacking noise. A screaming of brakes as a car slews round a corner at top speed might be a good comparison. Hers came in short waves, though there were variations according to the circumstance. It was a very loud, piercing and intimidating sound. Even Alsatians backed off hurriedly when they met it. This happened when some dog

76

jumped into the water in front of her and started splashing about. She immediately made a furious leap forward with one very short scream, then satisfying herself that he'd got the message, she left it at that and went on swimming, leaving the dog looking at her from the safer distance of the bankside.

Children playing in her stream and muddying it up had the same effect on her but the screams were more piercing for she began to work herself up into a frenzy; the noise was perfectly horrible and very embarrassing. She scuffed at the ground excitedly, started scrabbling in rushes or tussock grass, screaming until I calmed her down, told her off and otherwise shut her up.

When she saw the milkman, gas-man or electricity-man through the glass door and knew she couldn't get at them she gave vent to her rage in this same alarming fashion. Fortunately, she immediately responded to my 'Be quiet!' as I pulled her around and talked sharply to her. At this she became submissive, asked for reassurance and groaned. As soon as I left her, however, to go and see out the meter-reader, she began this furious screaming again.

I sensed the wildness in her at such moments, the real aspect of untameability and I understood why non-domestic animals, after long contact with humans and having lost their fear of them, will always be unpredictable. Natural attack fights for territory, food, mates, seem codified in comparison; certain laws seem to be obeyed, in the same way as those primitive tribes in New Guinea carried out their highly ritualized wars. But what has gone wrong with 'tamed' animals which leap to attack humans, could be that apart from the fact that they have become over familiar with the species, the animal has been too long separated from the pack, clan, or its family discipline with its own laws of behaviour and thus a necessary measure of order and control is lost.

This made me feel very depressed again, and especially when I thought about another noise she made, very similar to the squeak squeak, but softer, tenser, more excited, sharper. These sounds she made when sniffing a friend of ours in Bangkok, just before she bit him on his leg. We had expected her to make an attack scream warning, but she didn't, she just made these tense little squeaks.

So back to a happier sound, for instance, that important and heartening 'hah!' which ranged from the whispered query 'Hah?' to a loud, explosive, excited greeting sound. It was a soft 'Hah?' if she was not quite sure it was me 'Hah!' I'd say back and *'hah!'* she'd reply, relieved, joyful almost. It's nice to hear two otters 'Hah!' to each other.

Of course other types of otter have quite different vocabularies. If you said 'Hah!' to an English *lutra*, he'd wonder what you were on about.

Just to complete the description, she weighed five kilos, which was one too much, but she would thin down when I got her a mate organised somewhere where she couldn't be forever fridge thumping. She was very fit, strong, muscular and glossy.

It was late now, the pub-goers had long since gone home. Owlphonso was quiet too. I went upstairs to get my quota of sleep. And oh, by the way, Stinkerbelle had dreams. She would say 'eeh!' and jerk in her sleep and if she was round my feet I'd have to kick her and tell her it was all right. And another thing, sometimes Stinkerbelle snored.

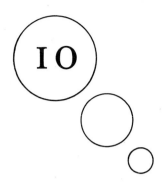

All scientific things were now forgotten because Forbes suddenly telephoned to say he could get back for two weeks. It was eleven o'clock before I got this good news digested and the Sunday newspapers read which meant that Stinkerbelle and I were late out for our park walk. On fine weather Sundays this could be harassing or interesting, depending on the circumstances.

'Oo-er, look, Mum!'

'Cor, look at that!'

'It's a badcher!'

'No, it's a ferret.'

'It's a *beaver!*'

'Run and ask the lady wot it is, George!'

Thunder of running feet, a shrill voice. Stinkerbelle turned aggressively.

'Miss! Miss!'

I wrapped Stinkerbelle's long lead around my hand so she was held close.

'Yes?'

'Wot is it, please?'

'An otter.'

'Hey, Mum! It's an *o'er!*'

Stinkerbelle did a little dance on her back feet, humping herself up and scuffing at the ground with her front ones. Then she gave an angry, high-pitched squeak; a short one because I bent down to stroke

79

her head. I coaxed her round and we went on, followed closely by George, a stubby little fellow with freckles.

'Where cha get 'im?'

'From Thailand.'

'Whas'e eat?'

'She eats fish and meat. *No!* I wouldn't touch her.'

George was joined by his sister. She had a high, shrill voice, 'Wha's 'is name?'

'Her name is, er, Stinkerbelle the Nark. *No*, don't come *too* close.'

'Coo-er, that's a funny name! Does she bite?'

Stinkerbelle was keeping her eye on them.

'Yes she might. You see, she doesn't know you.'

'Did she cost much?'

'Not really.'

'Can you get 'em here?'

'I shouldn't really. If you'd just keep a little bit away, you see she . . . I mean, if you'd just *move* so we can get past. That's right!'

'I saw her in the wa'er.'

'Yes, she likes swimming.'

'Yeah. Does she live at your place?'

'Yes.'

'Does she ever catch fish?'

'Sometimes. Small ones.'

'My dad catches *big* fish.'

'He'd need to. He's much bigger, isn't he?'

They started giggling and Stinkerbelle gave a warning whine. The mother called, 'George, Mary, come on now! Don't worry the lady!'

Stinkerbelle wanted to race after them but I dragged her off in another direction.

Very early in the morning, or on cold, wet, windy or misty days we rarely met anyone in the park except maybe for the one or two regulars; for instance the lady who looked after and tried to find homes for dogs people were tired of, didn't want anymore or had simply abandoned. She was a kind and cheery person, obviously enjoying her walks as much as the dogs. They all looked very happy.

I usually saw a couple of other dog owners, an occasional horse-rider and a bird-watcher or two. One of these watchers used to be in the park very early every summer morning, studiously noting and identifying the park birds. He was always most interested in Stinker-belle and one morning got his whole family out and brought them to the park to see her. 'Up at the crack of dawn he got us!' one of them said.

In spring, summer and early autumn I would often see the shep-herdess getting her flock together, or maybe the park gamekeeper with his gun and dog on a squirrel and crow culling expedition. One morning he probably wished he hadn't met us. I'd heard a baby duckling cheeping rather piteously in the drain overflow that leads from the lower Pen Pond into the water course. Having told him about this, the poor chap then felt it his duty to very kindly and bravely plunge waist-deep into cold water in order to rescue the little thing.

But if the park was deserted on early mornings and in bad weather, on fine Saturdays and Sundays cars filled the car parks and there were masses of people who came out to enjoy the rustic landscape. And if for some reason, usually the Sunday papers, I was late, we met dozens of them, not to mention their dogs : a regular cross-section of both.

Next I was approached by a middle-aged lady with her poodle. 'Oh, I've never seen one before! Dicky come here! Here, *wait*, I've told you! *No*, you'll leave it *alone*, you bad boy!' She put the dog's lead on and I didn't say anything because poodles when over-excited are apt to bounce and bark and generally carry on. 'May I look?' she asked, holding firmly on to Dicky.

'Of course!'

She looked. 'It *is* an otter, isn't it?'

'Yes.'

'Well I never! What a darling! Dicky, keep still! She *is* enjoying it, isn't she? Oh, look at her!'

'Yes, she likes to swim here.'

'Well that's made my day!'

Next came the sound of hooves. Stinkerbelle got out of the stream, stood upright on her back legs, surveyed the landscape and saw the horse. Into her line of vision came four large legs and in her olfactory line, a strong smell which once or twice she'd made a soft tentative Hah! noise to. The first horse was joined by a second. 'Oh look!' a rider said, 'an otter! What a gorgeous little thing. Do you often bring her for walks? Is she difficult to keep?'

'Well yes, more so than a dog which is looked after properly.'

'Oh, how heavenly! Look, she's standing up. *Look* at that!' And after watching her a while, off they went in a thunder of hooves.

We went up to the second lake. Two big labradors saw her and started leaping away from their owners. The owners had seen her too but they didn't call their dogs back. Stinkerbelle had just got into the water and as the dogs bounded up, she put her head over the bank and waited. The dogs were a little put out because what they were chasing was now sizing them up. There was quite a discrepancy in the sizes. The owners called once or twice, but it made not the slightest difference. The dogs started edging in on her, one at each side, sniffing, ready to continue with the chase. One of them barked, trying to make her get out and run. The other made a splashy leap into the water; this was too much for Stinkerbelle. She didn't like dogs splashing into her lake. She gave a sudden attack scream, flipped round and raced at the labrador. I hauled her back firmly, but the dog made an undignified retreat, looking a bit shamefaced.

'There! That'll teach you, Skeeter!' his owner called and added, 'They won't hurt her, they're as gentle as . . . ' Stinkerbelle gave another attack scream and leapt at the second dog which had dared put its foot in the water.

'Goodness!' said one of the owners, 'She can look after herself, can't she!'

'It's just a warning,' I said. 'When she gets to know a dog, she enjoys playing with it. In Bangkok she used to play really roughly with a dog about the size of yours.'

'Is that so?' The owners were comforting their dogs. A few more questions and on we went round the pond.

I didn't really notice what the dog owners looked like. After a while one notices their dogs but rarely the owners. But at the next stop there was a family and I noticed the children because they crowded in. Sometimes the parents would not say anything at all to their offspring as they practically *stood* on the otter or tried to stroke her (a natural instinct, of course, since she was rather cuddly looking) but, after I said as kindly as possible, 'If you wouldn't mind keeping back just a little,' for the third time and the parents still hadn't reined in their young, I pulled Stinkerbelle away and we made a hurried forward-march out of range.

But most children were really marvellous. They asked intelligent questions, kept their distance, were quiet and didn't shriek, yell or jump up and down. Quite often I'd hear a parent say, 'Oh look Tommy, a seal!' as Stinkerbelle bounded along the bank. And the youngster would chime back, 'No, it's an otter!'

Stinkerbelle was often called a badger, notwithstanding the fact that she was such a different size and badgers' heads have a very distinctive black and white marking. But a badger she was until the correction was made.

It's odd, though, the impression children, people in general or simply their voices create when they catch sight of a strange animal. One mostly feels an immediate sympathy, a deep interest in animals and wild life, and delight in watching the animal enjoying itself. Then there are the curiosity hunters who don't see it as a living animal but some *thing* to engage their curiosity. One might get the same reaction if one were tugging along a dead cat! One feels the egocentricity of such types. Fortunately they are rare.

But the photographer was one such. Many people asked me if they could take photos and I was always willing and pleased to let them try to snap her. However, I always felt rather sour about those who came racing up and without a by-your-leave started clicking away in a frantic sort of panic to get something out of the ordinary on their film.

This particular photographer was surrounded by a little entourage of people all of whom seemed to defer to him. He had what looked like a very expensive camera and was leaping around clicking this and that with that too-careless aplomb which often accompanies flattery, wealth or fame. He was rather handsome actually so I wished he could have been more sympathetic. Out of the corner of my eye I saw him coming towards me. He did a bounding little jump over a tussock and started clicking. It annoyed me. I led Stinkerbelle into the reeds and looked up. 'I say,' I said, 'if you asked you know . . . ' and felt a shudder of, was it horror? run through the little group. 'I *never* ask,' he said and leapt backwards still clicking while I shoved Stinkerbelle under a deep bank.

Later, as I cycled home I saw the same photographer taking close-ups of stags, with yet another photographer taking photos of him. So I wondered a bit. It wasn't anyone I knew though.

The last time Stinkerbelle got much attention from a photographer was *very* early one morning. The park was deserted, except for its wild life and us, when suddenly there came into view the astounding sight of four Japanese men plus movie camera. Then more astoundingly, one of the men began prancing around in karate-like attitudes by the lakeside. The movie men got down to recording this but stopped what they were doing as soon as Stinkerbelle squeaked at them. They gathered around and very politely asked me if they could include her in a film of their hero performing his limbering-up exercises in a London park. So Stinkerbelle was featured for a brief instance on a film destined for Japanese television.

But on this particular morning, we continued meeting more dogs; Alsatians, bulldogs, terriers, mongrels, sheep dogs, dachshunds, and whatever type they were, they all got much the same sort of warning treatment if they bounded at her, splashily leapt in the water in front of her, barked, or came bouncing up ready for a chase.

Sometimes though, Stinkerbelle showed a friendliness and tolerance towards strange dogs. Indeed, she seemed to react to some dogs as one reacts to some people, finding an almost immediate sympathy. For some she had only a sniff, some she was curious about and was quite gentle in her approach as if she would have liked to have made friends and play. Others she ignored completely or took a long look at before getting on with whatever she was doing. Pekinese aroused the worst in her.

As we continued our walk, I was amazed at the way Stinkerbelle

84

seemed to take it as a personal insult if people walked along a path in front of her. Even if they were yards away, she would squeak imperiously and strain on after them. Sometimes, and indeed with those park runners, this was a decided advantage for me since it got us along much more quickly. Once having passed the group or person though, she would ignore them and settle down to her usual gallop.

To a large extent she ignored people too, rolling in the grass to dry herself, or getting on with digging along the banks while the usual question and answer routine went on.

There were plenty of people sunning themselves on the benches near the water's edge that morning. An old man got up when he saw Stinkerbelle swimming along at the end of her lead and said, 'Well, well, what a funny little thing! Does it like sweets?' offering me a paper bag.

I refused a sweet but thanked him all the same.

Then a couple of rather strait-laced-looking female middleagers with stout boots and walking sticks spied her. 'Ah! An otter! Look Mabel, an otter.' They stopped me to ask about her. Stinkerbelle was swimming in a deep pool so she didn't mind the hold up.

'She's not an English otter, is she?' they asked.

'No,' I said, brightening up at such knowledge. 'She comes from Thailand and is a short-clawed type.'

'We've otters down in our part of Devon, you know.'

'Really? How marvellous.'

'Yes, we have hunts down there.'

'What?'

'Oh it's *very* interesting. The dogs have to be trained to it, of course.'

'Good *God*!' I said.

'Pardon?'

'You mean you train dogs to . . . and watch while . . . and club to death if . . . ?'

'Well of course they *do* have to be kept down, the fishing you see . . . '

'But I've been told on excellent authority they prefer eels and coarse fish, thereby protecting finer fish from such predators. They're getting scarce and if any good field research can prove otherwise, then there should be humane methods of culling them!'

'But it's always been done in our parts. Like fox hunting really.'

Stinkerbelle got out of the water and rolled herself dry. She looked charming when she did this.

'She's very nice,' said Mabel.

'She's lucky not to be an English otter in your part of Devon,' I said a bit sniffily and stroked Stinkerbelle's head. I suppose some people can club an animal to death after setting dogs on it, but it seems to me a sort of nasty barbarism, much like bear baiting, a sadistic sort of thing we could do without.

'She is sweet,' said Mabel watching Stinkerbelle roll around again and wave her paws in the air. As they couldn't equate Stinkerbelle and the cruel and barbaric practices on English otters their perverted sense of enjoyment led them to, we left it at that and muttering to myself, Stinkerbelle and I passed on.

There were more people. 'Oh is she tame?' 'She's your pet, is she?' 'What does it eat?' 'Where does it come from?' 'Where do you keep her?' 'How old is she?' 'Oh we've heard about the otter in the park,' (this one very common now). And those who insisted, much to my horror, on trying to touch and stroke her.

Then we came across a couple of fishermen who had caught a large pike. They watched Stinkerbelle, asked me about her eating habits and we were presented with that lovely fresh fish!

We crossed to the small pool to rest for a while. Stinkerbelle tried to dive into my bag to locate the origin of the fishy smell. Then suddenly we were surrounded by about eight people: a large family group. I had my back to them and I was tired so I continued to stare reflectively into the water. Stinkerbelle got in for a swim, but as I gazed at her, I felt the whole family grouped around my back silently staring at both of us. After a while I began to feel somewhat freakish so we moved off.

On the way back, we met the blind lady on horse-back. Her sister was riding alongside. They reined in their horses. 'How is she today?' 'Oh, she's standing up!' 'Hello!' Stinkerbelle's actions were described in detail before they moved off.

86

Finally we got back to my bicycle, and Stinkerbelle did her rolling-on-her-towel act which was immensely amusing to a little group of onlookers. Then the *coup de théâtre* as I lifted her up and dumped her in the bicycle basket where she sat with paws over the edge looking at everyone, or giving her back another little scratch against the wicker work.

Sunday mornings in the park generally followed this pattern unless I got up exceptionally early, or took the lesser known paths and quieter byways. I do hope that those hundreds of people who saw her in the park and to whom I spoke about her had as much pleasure in seeing her as I had in their interest. I think she made people's walks in the park just that much more enjoyable and their concern certainly made me feel much more optimistic regarding the attitude to wild life in general, and in particular the conservation of otters.

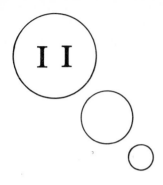

I I

Forbes got home for two weeks. Stinkerbelle greeted him with warm exuberance and we all went for walks in the park together. We had decided that it would be best to find a temporary home for her: it was just too difficult to attempt carting an otter from A to B, or maybe C to D when perhaps B and D wouldn't accept her anyway. I had already rung up countless zoos and private people who might, but couldn't: and she *did* need a mate wherever she was. Also, I wasn't going to just dump her anywhere. However, Forbes and I were both optimistic that a solution could be found.

Soon after Forbes left, I took up the telephone again, following a new lead. The reply was, Yes, there is someone interested in having her. Could I go up and see him? I did. He was interested but didn't have an enclosure ready and he was going off on a longish journey. He never saw Stinkerbelle.

The next proposition was a wild life park, some hours from London. Two amblonyx otters had just arrived at the zoo, the curator informed me. I wondered if I could bring Stinkerbelle up to meet his pair. 'Certainly,' he said.

Stinkerbelle in her travelling cage narked all the way. Buster the dachshund looked ashamed that any animal could make such a disgusting noise, while my kind neighbour drove us stoically on to our destination.

The park was closed to the public at this time of the year and seemed deserted. After a while, however, the curator was found and introduced to Stinkerbelle who was enjoying herself dabbling around in the mud.

We all went inside the long stable block and made for the otters' domain : a small but adequate holding enclosure with a thick covering of straw on the floor, a large water bowl and sleeping hutch.

'Usually we put a new arrival next door so they can see and get to know each other through the wire first,' the curator said. I agreed, but as we approached the chain link door, Stinkerbelle, excited now, stood against it and said, 'Hah!' There was an answered greeting from the hutch : two small heads appeared. Stinkerbelle said 'Hah!' again and they Hah-ed back at her.

'Perhaps it will be all right,' I said. 'As you like,' said the curator.

I opened the door and dragged a reluctant Nark in after me. She was quite right to be reluctant since it was not her territory. I carried her sponge mat and her spraint tray into the enclosure as well, hoping that familiar smells would help her more readily assert herself.

For a few minutes all was quiet. Everyone seemed to be waiting for the first move to be made. Two pairs of eyes were still peering at us from the hutch and Stinkerbelle stayed close to me as we waited for curiosity to overcome apprehension.

Five minutes later with a loud 'Hah!' a head jack-in-the-boxed out of the hutch entrance, snorted and rapidly withdrew again. Another few minutes of tense and watchful waiting before one young otter, the female, came out to reconnoitre. She was bolder and more inquisitive than her mate who, preferring to put up with the suspense, watched her every move from the hutch.

This little female reminded me of Tonka, the young otter we had tried unsuccessfully to introduce to Stinkerbelle and her mate on their territory in Bangkok. The females of amblonyx do seem to be more outward going, more apt to explore, play and get into mischief. The male, on the other hand, was like our Charlie in Bangkok, more suspicious, head up, his expression serious, very much on his dignity and almost haughtily vigilant.

The female spent some time cautiously circling us, getting closer and closer until suddenly, with a quick dart forward she sniffed at

90

Stinkerbelle who, wedged firmly between my large winter boots, gave a short, resentful warning. The squeak from the female as she leapt back was echoed by a startled snort from the male looking on from a distance.

But the female was getting bolder and with courage to match her curiosity was soon dodging around my boots while Stinkerbelle, hunched up between them, watched her suspiciously, expecting to be pestered at any moment. All this was too much for the male and soon he decided to join in the investigation and to see exactly what his mate was up to.

They were both much smaller and younger than Stinkerbelle, hardly more than cubs in fact; nonetheless, she would not leave the safety of my boots as unwillingly she put up with their examination. I felt sorry for her; for here she was grouchy, yet quite submissive, waiting to see if she'd survive the interview and win their approbation, or at least, their tolerance. What a change from the usual bouncing bit of narky bossiness!

Meanwhile the investigation went on : inquiring or startled squeaks from the pair, then a low surly groaning sound from Stinkerbelle when they came too close. If I moved, the pair would snort and dive back into their hutch again.

After about an hour however, when they had become used to my presence, I managed to get my feet away from Stinkerbelle, unclip her lead and move quietly back to the wall leaving her open to their overtures.

As soon as the two of them began whiskering her she lay on her back submissively, but still looked rather huffy about it all, or as if affronted that two such young otters should dare to take liberties with her. She turned over then, squeaked back at them, or gave a growly, Eerh! when they nudged her.

She was at this time, I believe, in the fairly interesting state of a short heat period. The male got bolder, his mate quite cheeky, but neither seemed really aggressive and soon Stinkerbelle, losing her sulky passivity, went gambolling around in the straw as if she owned the place. She ignored them as she sniffed at their spraint, drank from their water trough, rolled on her sponge mat, or inspected their empty food dish.

The two young otters followed her closely until the female, intrigued with her harness, snapped at it, trying to pull it off. Stinkerbelle gave one cross *eerh!* sound and the two withdrew at once. At that moment she looked like the rather annoyed mother of two young cubs. Indeed, the situation seemed so promising that I slipped off her harness and managed to get out of the enclosure before she realized what I was up to. Hiding behind a bale of straw I awaited further development, ready to dash in at a moment's notice to rescue any otter which might need assistance.

Two minutes later Stinkerbelle gave up trying to get out and stopped complaining about being left alone. She went over to survey the sleeping box, climbed on top, whiffled all over it, then got down again to lie on her towel, scuffing it up, rolling around in it: she seemed to be inviting the younger two to join her in a game. The female took one corner of the towel and started dragging it off into their sleeping hutch, Stinkerbelle allowed her to do it, being busy grooming herself, ignoring them again.

The male was trying to push a piece of stick under her sponge mat. It all looked very peaceful, and feeling confident I left the otters together while the curator showed me the new otter enclosure they were in the process of making.

An old brick wall ran down one side. There was a huge tree with gnarled surface roots, and at one end a bush and bamboo thicket. The pool would be near the front, the ground turfed and there would be a stone wall, low enough to look over on three sides. And a sand or soft earth pit? I asked, because they love digging and some logs to play round and perhaps some tussocky grass mixed in with the turf and er . . .

'We'll see.'

So my enthusiasm was silenced. After all, it was probably irritating for a curator to have suggestions poured at him from an amateur and one of those damn people with their *pets*!

'And of course she'll eat exactly the same food as our otters eat,' he informed me sternly. I took his point. All curators are suspicious of ex-pets and are justified in this since the animal has usually become over familiar with humans, has been spoilt and so on: all this applied to Stinkerbelle. But it was agreed that I should bring her up again in three weeks, for a few days this time, to verify that the tolerance the pair had shown towards her was going to continue. By that time it was hoped the enclosure would be well on the way.

Work on the enclosure had been held up by rain, but after a month had passed, I decided to go up anyway and sit with the otters for some days to make sure they really *were* going to accept Stinkerbelle. I was still dubious. After all, Charlie – Stinkerbelle's Bangkok mate – had most decidedly refused to accept a new female on his territory.

It was a very cold day but Stinkerbelle, having had a large meal and therefore feeling lively, was getting excited and reluctant and excited again as we made for the door.

'Hah!' This time the reaction was more definite: the female came bounding out and over to us at once while the male followed more guardedly. We had a repeat of the dodging-round-my-shoes procedure. This time, however, the squeaks were louder and Stinkerbelle sought my protection every minute. I'd brought her otter-smelling sponge mat and her spraint tray into the room again, but she lay between my feet looking as if she'd known happier times and was regretting them. She squashed herself up trying to appear smaller and less conspicuous.

The little female sniffed, squeaked and had an indignant look about her; her mate held back, alert and watchful. But the reactions were quite different from the first time. The pair looked bigger, much less timid. Then the male began to whisker around my feet too, taking a tentative bite at one of my shoes and helping the female to upset Stinkerbelle still further by continually circling, sniffing and squeaking.

In one month they had developed fast, had lost their nervousness and had become much more assertive. Indeed, the male was nudging Stinkerbelle's tail now and as soon as I lifted my foot off the ground, she, more exposed, rolled on her back with her paws in the air in an attitude of complete and dismal subjection.

93

A worrying situation; the reaction was correct as far as the otters were concerned and what one might have expected, but it was all wrong as far as I was concerned and what the first introduction had led me to expect. The female came forward again to begin a determined exploration. Stinkerbelle immediately lay back, inviting bites on her most vulnerable patches. Once she gave a warning Eerh! at which the male, having sniffed over his female to make sure she was all right, then started off on a stern and censorious investigation of the newcomer. This time he wasn't exactly friendly.

Obviously he had decided that two females were going to be more than he could cope with and he showed his disapprobation again with a couple of loud squeaks and a token bite near the tender base of her tail. Stinkerbelle made a low, half-warning, complaining noise which didn't express much conviction and she was still in a position of desolated capitulation, lying there, sadly shivering, letting herself be nosed, pushed at and token bit again. By this time I was bending over them to be quite sure the bites were falling just short of the fur, but it wasn't too pleasant. The female made no attempt to bite, although she did most of the sniffing.

Then as if he'd shown Stinkerbelle where she stood, or rather lay in his establishment, the male relaxed, made another short inspection of his female and began grooming her.

I sat down. Stinkerbelle curled up between my feet, but I soon shifted to leave her exposed again. The female, curious, energetic and getting more familiar every minute, began examining my shoes, my hands and coat, demanding attention.

I gave her a ping-pong ball and was fascinated to see how quickly she learnt to play with it, holding it in between her back paws, shoving it up over her stomach into her front ones, then juggling it down to her back paws again. She was a lovely, lively little animal.

Stinkerbelle stayed curled up. She was not very interested in life anymore. I stroked her or talked to her encouragingly and later, seeming less depressed about the situation, she began to respond to the young female's overtures. Once or twice I thought they might get friendly, but whenever Stinkerbelle sniffed back or complained, the male leapt up to make an excited, explosive and snorty noise, telling her to leave his mate alone.

The curator appeared. 'How's it going?'

'The male doesn't really relish the idea of having another female, I'm afraid. Actually, it's a repeat of an experience we had with three otters in Bangkok,' and I told him the story. 'We tried for a long time,' I said, 'but it didn't make any difference, the new female was always ostracised by the male. I thought that Stinkerbelle being so much more mature might overrule this one. It looked so hopeful the first time but perhaps she was on heat then.'

'Oh well, you never know.'

Three days later I did. The situation had got progressively worse. With the female, Stinkerbelle was slightly less servile, but the male reduced her to a nervous state of dejected submission. They would not allow her to eat any food and although I experimented by not feeding her and getting her quite hungry she dared not go near the tray when they were there. She was now getting token bites from the male whenever she moved. I tried leaving her alone with them for long periods for I was fairly sure the male really wouldn't bite her, but the gestures he made were bad enough.

On the last day, the curator agreed to an experiment. If we could put Stinkerbelle in another room, get her used to it, sprainting in it, eating and generally making it her territory before introducing the other two to *her*, it might work. I helped prepare another stable room, then led Stinkerbelle in. She rushed around on the straw like her old self, investigating it as was her wont in strange places. I put some spraint here and there and gave her some food which she proceeded to munch with a hungry return of appetite. But she had been in this new room for only ten minutes, when to my horror, two burly keepers came in and dropped the little male and female in their sleeping hutch in with us.

'I say!' I said. 'Couldn't you leave it for a while?' But they were already disappearing down the corridor.

Stinkerbelle was her old assertive self for approximately five minutes after that. The little male had by this time, explored the territory, sprainted and they had both eaten a piece of Stinkerbelle's fish. Then, turning his attention to her, he reduced her to her previous doleful attitude; curled up, trembling and totally submissive. Soon, he would threaten to bite her whenever she showed the least sign of moving.

My neighbour's sister kindly drove up and collected us.

'Well,' I said, 'it was great to watch two otters together again. They're really a lovely pair.' The curator had said that if I managed to get a mate for Stinkerbelle, then he would agree to put the four otters in the new enclosure at the same time. Since no otter would have presumed prior right over the territory, this could well be a solution, Stinkerbelle would have a mate and the enclosure would be large enough to accommodate two pairs.

'But,' I said to Stinkerbelle that night as she bounced joyfully and bossily from chair to bed and got bounced back again, 'whatever happens, we'll certainly get you a mate! Actually I feel as if I've been ostracised too.' Whereupon I turned over to switch out the light and she burrowed down to my feet, going to sleep with her paws firmly gripped round my ankles. I felt a bit shackled. Then she had nightmares.

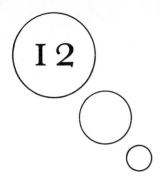

12

Getting a mate for Stinkerbelle the Nark was a problem. The large ethical question of getting involved with a dealer presented itself.

Literally thousands upon thousands of living animals are subjected to abominable suffering and cruel death because (a) there is in the U.K. and the U.S.A. such a demand for wild animals and (b) because poachers, middlemen, transporters, dealers, all immersed in counting their financial gain, are callously unaware, or perhaps conveniently unaware, that they are dealing with intensely alive creatures capable of gentleness, affection, suffering, fear, shock, tenderness and love.

Of course there are many factors animals do not share with us, the highest developed of all mammals: sadism, monetary greed, power complexes and the underlying deeper frustrations which make it a 'satisfying' experience for people to horrifically illtreat animals.

How we care about animals is a measure of our humanity and our degree of civilization which must be based upon a humane approach to *all* living things. For if one considers simply the life in a single leaf, one must recognise in the movement of sap the miracle of evolution which has taken an unimaginable time to create. Humility should spring from this and a recognition of the preciousness of life from the simplest cell to the most complex creation. Only on the basis of this recognition and on this humility can there be hope for a saner humankind.

But thousands upon thousands of once-living beings, from small birds to the apes and the great cats, arrive at airports in the U.K. and the

U.S.A. dead from suffocation, shock, malnutrition, subjection to extreme heat, cold and thirst; their dead and dying bodies are found squashed up in impossibly small and airless boxes. Although a ban was imposed on the import of exotic animals in the U.K. unless quarantine regulations could be met, the traffic still goes on today. It is ironic that these two countries with all their societies to help wild animals, with all their high-powered patronage and publicity are those which cause the most destruction and the most suffering to animals.

Otters too are now subject to quarantine restrictions, but at the time I decided to get Stinkerbelle a mate they were not. I was loath to acquire a male otter through a dealer. Even to transport an otter from Thailand was causing enough soul-searching. The animals we had in Thailand were kept pending their release to the wild. That Stinkerbelle the Nark had reached such a stage of dependence and had bossily organised herself into our life so deeply that it was impossible to get her to go back to the wild made me feel guilty enough. One lives and learns. A large responsibility would be added to the situation if I did get her a mate, for then optimum conditions would have to be found to give them both the best possible life.

Fortunately, I had friends in Bangkok who would try their best to help find a male otter already in captivity, one needing better living conditions. I wrote to them setting out the problem, asked them to supervise the freight caging if they were successful, and sent the letter off at once.

And the postal strike began.

Meanwhile, up at the wild life park they were proceeding with the outside enclosure. 'It's getting on very nicely,' the curator informed me. I thought of the postal strike, the time delay, the impossibility of settling Stinkerbelle in the park if her mate did not arrive in time and what I would do if . . . But, 'It's no use sitting here worrying!' I said to a comfortably cushioned Nark. 'Come on! Rally!' And I hastened to take her out for a walk in the autumn park.

The colours changed from day to day : the park scenes were never the same, they changed with the weather, with the season, even with one's moods. Seagulls had come now for the winter, wheeling over the pools,

98

shrieking, diving or following the plough, clustering along the lines of freshly-turned earth; vociferous, seldom still, white wings against the rich brown soil or fluttering against the heavy autumn clouds.

There was a wealth of glowing colour across fields of ochre, burnt amber, sage green. The yellows turning to russet around the greens of the bracken, bowed now to the colder weather. Gone were the blue silhouettes of trees on the hill seen beyond a haze of summer grasses. The migrant birds too were going, flocking, preparing to depart, settling for a while to feed on the fields before continuing south. The crows' kraak had a lonely sound, but the squirrels were still busy.

There were plenty of fallen chestnuts on the hill grove and Stinker-belle should have been careful where she put her feet, but she wasn't so I had to guide her round the prickly husks. When I said 'Stop!' she stopped dead. The nettles and thistles had almost disappeared; one less problem for her feet. She liked playing with or gnawing at the

smooth chestnuts themselves so I gathered some for her. I also collected pieces of old wood for the parrots to chew into and some of the special seed heads they liked.

And all around us the colours glowed; oak, chestnut, hawthorn, aspen, poplar, willow; chrome yellow, orange, browns, scarlet and a mosaic of colour under one's feet, or seen swirling with bits of drift wood in the water course.

A white horse galloped away in the distance. T. S. Eliot, I said to myself and followed Stinkerbelle up to the lake where sedge and reed were fading and the water reflected an autumn sky. Then a swan broke the reflection as it took off from the water; a great flapping effort across the lake, a desperate sounding whirr of wings. It rose, slowly as a dream, heavily gaining height; the big body, the neck stretched out and the sound of its flight echoing into the still air. The deeper, under bank water looked black, but a yellow reflection glowed here and there. Chestnuts and autumn leaves were washed up along the edges. There was a touch of bright red and a vivid green in the clothes of two small boys searching for conkers.

Over to the small pool next and I remembered how, three mornings ago, we came across two stags standing mid-pool, startled by our approach; magnificent antlers on raised heads, mist hanging in the hollow, the great oaks towering above. No wind to play in the dying leaves or disperse the mist, and the birds were silent: a legendary moment.

I liked watching the park deer; red or fallow. And during the sorting-out season there were some magnificent fights. Red stags antler to antler; the thrust and push of strong bodies straining to force one another back, the low moo-roars from the throats, the click-click of the antlers, then the break away of one stag with head held high and a wild look in his eyes. There were the mud wallows which Stinkerbelle, fascinated by the smell of deer, always wanted to explore.

Once, by the chestnut grove hill, I saw a large herd of fallow deer gathered together in the evening light. This was no unusual sight in itself but suddenly, breaking away from the group, a handsome stag determinedly walked away from the herd with that head-nodding movement; he very deliberately walked along a path in the bracken, then down the hill through the grass. He was soon followed by another stag. The first hesitated, the other hastened to catch up. They walked together, side by side about four feet apart, antlers nodding in unison. But all at once, without warning and as if at some preconceived signal, both turned, locked antlers and began to fight. The struggle went on for about three minutes, then both walked on again, slowly, heads nodding, side by side, four feet apart until a repeat of the sudden turn, the loud click-click and the straining, heaving bodies.

A young stag left the herd and ran towards them. He was ignored. Another ran down and chased the first back. Meanwhile, like duellists observing strict laws, the two assailants continued their march across the field. It was near sunset; grass and bracken were touched with fiery colour, the trees beyond went smokey black and the stags locked antlers again.

But this particular day the deer herds were quiet in the distance as Stinkerbelle cruised down the water course searching for her frog. It seemed to have disappeared but she swam and dolphined down the full water course not seeming to find the water too cold yet. Once or twice during the autumn there had been so much rain that the course had filled up to the very top of its banks and in some places had over-flowed. Big puddly lakes and ponds appeared in the fields. I wore my gumboots to slosh through them and Stinkerbelle wallowed and dug and swam, having a marvellous time.

The days went by through the rain. The postal strike went on, weeks began to add up and nervously I called the curator at the wild life park. 'Oh, they're in their enclosure already,' he said, 'They're enjoying it immensely!'

'Oh well . . . '

He had sounded jovial and pleased about keeping them at least and I was glad that those two little otters should have such a good home. 'But Stinkerbelle,' I said, 'it'll be really their territory now, which means that's one wild life park you can't be parked in.'

Then I received a long communication from Forbes who was being

sent off to Guyana, Surinam and Venezuela among other places with a base at Georgetown where authorities thought it wasn't advisable to leave wives alone while husbands were off on travels.

I thought I might as well go to the theatre and some exhibitions to get my mind off animals in general and the problem of Stinkerbelle in particular. 'I won't be trapped by an otter!' I told her as I left her ice-bucket on the floor and fixed up the parrots with plenty of food and things to do and peck at.

Besides, I was fast becoming the local eccentric, or already had become. I had told some people I'd soon be off because Stinkerbelle would be settled in a wild life park. They probably thought I was also a little mad: and there goes our eccentric, riding on her rusty old bicycle, gum-booted, scruffy-coated and a peculiar kind of scarf holding her hair down, almost. And there's her otter in the basket, squeaking to the wind, waving her paws with some condescension at passers-by while her chauffeuse and general handmaid wheezes and gasps her way to the nearest duck pond. 'But it's not natural, my dear!'
'Grrr, Stinkerbelle!' I said. 'It's not as if we're all imprinted here. You're an independent little beast, I know, and as long as you *are* happy with a mate, good food, good playing and swimming conditions, I know you'll say, "I'm all right, Jack".'

Unfortunately though, I couldn't do the same. I had this awful sense of responsibility regarding her future. I *would* get her a mate and a good home. I wouldn't just dump her and hope for the best or, as some people suggested, have her put down as the easiest way out.

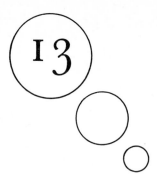

13

Bicycling along with the wind behind me and Stinkerbelle in front, I thought about the ways of narks: Stinkerbelle and Charlie Brown in Bangkok, then entered new female Tonka. Charlie wouldn't have her, Stinkerbelle was sour about it.

Stinkerbelle and the pair in the wild life park; male wouldn't have her, female was curious but not too aggressive. So far so good as expected reactions were concerned.

Then Stinkerbelle visited an adult pair with cubs on their territory; but here it was the female who was aggressive, rather frenziedly so. When the female and cubs were bundled out of the way, however, the *male* otter made seductive advances to Stinkerbelle bringing her presents like balls and sponge bags, finding her interesting and going to sleep curled up next to her. His mate screamed her jealousy in the background. Maybe Stinkerbelle was on heat that time though. Or maybe the female was more aggressive having cubs with her, or . . . But strange are the ways of otters and I bicycled into the park against the wind and didn't have time to give it more thought as the Nark was complaining and trying to burrow her head under my gloved hand on the handlebar.

After a wobble into a roadside post I deemed it better to get off. Stinkerbelle was tipped out and we struck off cross-country in an effort to keep under the lea of small hills and large oaks. My scarf came off, my hair almost did the same, and when I looked down to the right I saw a sheepskinned man leave his red Mini on the side of the road and start flapping in the wind over the fields in our direction.

Surely he wasn't trying to catch us up in this! I ploughed on. Stinkerbelle didn't present much resistance to wind because she was close to the ground and she was straining on the lead wanting to get on to her ponds. But that sheep-jacketed man was blowing up the side of the hill, yelling something like, 'Could I . . . ?' I didn't feel much like hanging around answering questions; strong cold winds tended to make me irritable.

The man approached. 'Would you mind?' I looked at him vaguely and he went on, 'My wife and I just saw you as we were passing in the car . . . I'm a press man, you see, and I thought it might be interesting to . . . It *is* an otter isn't it?'

Stinkerbelle turned to look at him. 'Yes,' I said, 'she is.'

'Well, I wonder if you'd mind if we did a story on her and took some pictures some time when you're . . . '

'Well I don't know,' I said grumpily, 'she doesn't like having her picture taken.'

'Tell you what, I'll give you a ring early next week and maybe we can arrange something.'

'Well maybe . . . ' He took my phone number and we left it at that, pushing off on our various windswept ways.

He rang the following Monday morning. 'Could I?' He had a press photographer friend who would take the pictures.

'Well, yes, maybe,' I said, 'if I can have copies of the photos. Is he a good photographer?'

They arrived the following Thursday morning. Both of them were rather young and quite nice after all. The photographer looked rather blasé and professional until Stinkerbelle attack screamed at him. Then he began to get interested in her as a photographic subject. I had got on my best jumper and had done my hair up into its going-out position.

We went into the back garden. I carried Stinkerbelle because I didn't want any press-man to get bitten, for goodness sake. 'Stinkerbelle quiet!' I said.

'Kiss her!' the photographer said.

'Eh?'

'Could you hold her up against your face more, that's it and kiss her or something?'

'Why? Otters don't *kiss!*'

'Well never mind, if you'd just hold her up against your face. That's it! Smile now! A *big* smile!' Click. Stinkerbelle, concertina-like squeezed up, was photographed from all angles with her face sour and mine tooth-filled.

Then we put her in the basket and leant the bicycle against the fence. She stood up in the basket, put her paws over the fence and looked over at him as he clicked again. He was getting enthusiastic now and I hoped he was making a good job of it. After this, we all drove off: the press in their car, me on bicycle to the common where I duti-fully turned circles and figures of eight and felt like a circus clown while the clicking went on. He was getting really keen now, lying flat on the muddy ground while we walked towards him: Stinkerbelle needed no coaxing to rush determinedly forward in his direction with that look in her eye.

After this we went off to the park. They put their car just inside the gates and prepared to leave it there. 'Well maybe you'll have to put it in the car park,' I said, as out of the corner of one eye I saw a lady park attendant. It was the one who had warned me about riding my bicycle on the grass one day so I knew they wouldn't stand a chance. But the press man was informing me, 'Oh, it'll be all right. We have our press cards. They always . . . ' when at that moment a voice interrupted with, 'You can't leave it there, you know!'

As he put the car in its proper place the photographer and I went down to the first little pool which we rarely visited as often there were people there. He clicked away at Stinkerbelle swimming, nosing the water, and digging under the roots of the big oak tree at the water's edge. I wondered why he wouldn't take more photos of Stinkerbelle on her own.

But a few more shots and it was all over. Stinkerbelle was glad. She'd had enough of being pulled around and put into position. Copies of photographs were promised, more information given. Yes, I was trying to find a temporary home for her and establish her with a

mate and so on. They told me that I should keep a look out in one of next week's morning papers.

I kept a look out. In fact, I bought the paper every day for a week. And every day it seemed to be full of cheese-cakey girls in bikinis, in minis or hotpants, patting, kissing, stroking langourously, and smiling at various animals, or simply looking as if they were out to seduce the camera.

'Well, if only I'd been a bit cheesier,' I said to Stinkerbelle. 'Why, you might have had your photo in the daily press and someone might have thought, What a lovely otter! and offer to look after you for a while.'

The photographer sent me a lovely batch of large photos. They were very good and I was very appreciative of the fact that he'd gone to so much trouble, although I wished he could have been more of an *animal* photographer.

Some time later someone said, 'I say, saw you the other day in the evening paper!' 'What?' 'Yes, big splash over one page.' 'Good heavens!' I said, and got some back copies to see what the reporter and photographer had been up to. To my relief, Stinkerbelle looked quite charming. I thought I looked rather healthy for me; all that walking, I decided.

When I read the text though I discovered that Stinkerbelle 'barked like a dog', which bit of information didn't thrill me too much. How on earth had they got that impression? 'Just shows you how they muddle things up,' I said as I rescued the drain cover and pulled Stinkerbelle out groaning her complaint like an angry lamb with tonsillitis; bark like a dog indeed!

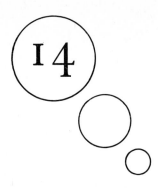

14

That it would be somewhat nervewracking I had no doubt, but only five minutes and a children's programme. It could do some good if there were any potential otter hunters among those children. A B.B.C. voice had rung up asking me if Stinkerbelle could feature in their *Blue Peter* programme.

My first visit to the studio was made without Stinkerbelle but with the film Forbes had made of her in a Thai National Park. Technicalities were discussed about a bicycle, a bath and a toy and fish supply. A short history and description of habits were also given.

The next step was rehearsal. Realizing that television people might be rather peculiar about punctuality, I decided to take Stinkerbelle for a very early walk, then after she'd eaten and had plenty to drink, get her to nap off in her travelling cage which she sometimes liked to sleep in anyway. This would give me time to get ready without a demanding Nark around my feet.

So far so good; she was sound asleep in her cage when I shut the door. Action and reaction: at once, a wide-awake otter was shoving, pulling, pawing, nosing, using all her strength to bulge the wire or get her paws, then her arms through.

'Look, just go to sleep again!' I said. 'I'm *not* taking you on a lead in a taxi, so there! I want to arrive somewhere looking and smelling respectable for once!'

Squeak, squeak, growl, utterly irate squeak after squeak. I threw a blanket over the cage, talked to her reassuringly, then ignored her until she finally settled down in her pile of woollen jerseys and scarves and such articles of clothing which once belonged to me and some of which were quite nice really before they got ottered off.

The taxi arrived. Stinkerbelle's travelling cage was lifted in and I followed up with the icebox of fish, spraint tray, leads, toys and drinking bowl. The Nark of course had been awake for some time and had not ceased to crossly demand her immediate release. When not mercifully asleep in a darkened travelling cage, Stinkerbelle expected everything the inside of a car contained to welcome her closest attention – every part, of course, included the driver's earholes.

The Nark was feeling awfully frustrated. From time to time a paw would push the blanket above the wire and the blanket would jiggle while angry screeches described extreme displeasure.

'*Cor!*' said the taxi driver feelingly and hastily closed off the window partition.

The Nark still complained. Perhaps it hadn't been a good idea to bring her in her travelling cage after all. Besides, when we arrived, there I was in some barren, patio-like, concrete enclosure trying to decide whether or not to leave the cage with Nark inside, spraint tray and fish box to themselves while I sprinted through doors to a reception counter in order to let the programme people know of our arrival.

I sprinted.

By the time I got back quite a few people were aware of our arrival anyway. Stinkerbelle had found a hole in the blanket, was pushing her paw through and accompanying the action with a frenzied and angry squeaking. 'What have you got there then, a tiger cub?' somebody asked.

There was, however, a slightly distressed sound in the squeaking. Oh Lord, I thought, not here. Not just when we're going to be met by . . . Stinkerbelle, can't you *wait!*

Not Stinkerbelle. The squeaks sounded more desperate. Knowing her sounds so well enabled me to distinguish between sheer irritability and real need. 'All right!' I said, let her out, clipped on her lead, drew her spraint tray out of the large plastic bag and plonked it down. 'Quick!' I said and kicked it in my usual impatient fashion.

When she'd finished, somebody applauded which I thought was rather cynical of them.

Stinkerbelle had stopped squeaking and was exploring the area around my feet while I wondered if I could ask someone if I could dump the tray in a B.B.C. courtyard, or would I have to carry it stinking through corridors. But there wasn't time to ask and I was just very carefully slipping the tray into the plastic carrier bag, keeping it horizontal all the way when a very polished but thankfully sympathetic man from the programme direction introduced himself and offered his assistance.

I ought to have washed my hands first before we shook them, but he was very charming about it and even gallantly struggled along the endless corridors and in and out of lifts with the large travelling cage and its tatty blanket. Stinkerbelle squeaked purposefully after his heels all the way while I tried to keep the plastic bag exactly on the level, cope with the strain on the lead and a Nark determined to get everyone out of her way as usual, and at the same time juggle with her fish box and water bowl.

I wondered how she was going to behave. I might have known though that she had star qualities. First of all her self-confidence and composure startled everyone. After depositing all her luggage in the star's dressing room, she led the way into the studio, eager to investigate every nook and cranny of it. Then she went through her paces like a fairly temperamental prima donna, making only one short attack screech when she found a strange hand almost within reach on a particularly comfortable and bouncy couch she would have liked to have taken over.

Otherwise she found the whole business refreshingly absorbing; new smells, sounds, objects, new toys, plenty of ping-pong balls and trips to the dressing room for freshening-up periods. I arrived home exhausted but the Nark was well satisfied with her day.

The next time we went was performance day. We started out at ten thirty in the morning. This time I left her cage at home and, sitting in the taxi, was bounced over by a squeaking otter all the way. The only time she stopped was when she felt hungry, demanded food and startled anyone travelling behind us by stretching out on her towel on the back sill of the taxi, resting on her elbows and chomping up fish.

Anything for peace and quiet, I thought. It was a different taxi driver, but the same expression was in his voice as he glanced through his rear vision mirror and said, '*Cor!*'

Stinkerbelle meanwhile wanted another piece of fish even before she'd finished getting her paws and nose clean, which meant that my jersey got fishbits on it and a strong smell about it.

I'll be glad when this is over, I thought. Besides which, there was the strain of wondering whether the Nark would get narky during the actual live performance time and do nothing at all.

Rehearsals went on at intervals all day so that we could be more optimistic about being word and deed perfect for the five minutes live performance after five p.m.

Between these rehearsals, Stinkerbelle led the way back to her very own dressing room where she settled down and relaxed, yawned around and thought it not so interesting as the studio where there were more wires, cables and interesting things to poke around in. Then up we went yet again for the last run through, Stinkerbelle knowing the route by this time, leading the way while people scattered in all directions.

A bicycle with basket was provided. She sat in it in her usual Cleopatra-Duchess-like way to be cycled into camera range with me trying to miss a strung-up plastic boat which was liable to poke my eye out if I wasn't careful. Next she was tipped out and got a large piece of trout which she proceeded to tuck into while she was talked about.

As I set next to the glamorously dressed young woman who was posing all the leading questions, I kept thinking of how I smelt of fish and how the smell tended to get stronger under the arc lights and I wished I'd been able to change into a borrowed jacket.

Stinkerbelle, having gorged herself on fish while we talked about her more endearing qualities, led the way over to the big bath tub provided. She climbed the steps, sniffed at the water, then slid in to swirl, splash, hook up balls and generally disport, enjoying herself so much she had to be dragged out.

Once out she dried herself on her towels, then played with ice

cubes and other favourite toys specially provided. Everything was
laid on for her. She had a large group of admirers and in fact she put
on such a good performance that the Thailand film was cut in order
to give the star full opportunity to make the most of her role. She ate
so much trout in between these rehearsals and during them that I
decided she would have to go on a semi-starvation diet for the next
week.

But suddenly there were two minutes to go before the live relay.
There had to be complete silence so I felt like coughing and could feel
Stinkerbelle getting fed up with sitting in a bike basket and not being
chauffeured anywhere. At any moment she was going to bossily squeak
me into action. I stroked and pushed her around playfully but she could
feel a slight tension in my hand and was all ready to order me about
when thankfully we got the signal to bicycle off around that plastic
boat.

Stinkerbelle only downed half her trout chunk since it was the tail
bit and she was definitely getting choosey by that time, but otherwise
she performed beautifully, everything went according to plan and some
lovely close-ups of her in action – eating, swimming and playing –
were taken.

We taxied home with ten more trout. Stinkerbelle was tired but had a
well-satiated look on her face. And for ever afterwards in the park, I
was asked, 'Didn't I see her on TV?'

Stinkerbelle, you're famous! I told her. Now all we have to do is to
get you a mate and let you get on with it.

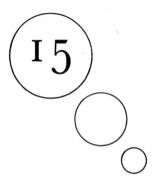

15

The postal strike was over and a letter arrived from Bangkok. My friends were kindly doing their best to locate and send a suitable male otter. Meanwhile, there was another wild life park interested in having Stinkerbelle but they were going to be months getting an enclosure ready. I bore it in mind and got on with this and that.

Winter was coming on fast. There were days in the park when we wandered tentatively through a shroud of mist and fog, a strange, lost landscape; the sudden gaunt of solemn oaks, stark, black branches ghosting into the mist, the kraak of the crows somewhere above and trees even close to looked far-off, flat silhouettes against a swirl and wraith of fog. A cold and bitter tang was in the air. Colours were washed out, faded from the fields, there were no squirrels and few birds. The water fowl huddled together under the threat of snow in the air, but Stinkerbelle still galloped along or swam the water course searching frogs and sticklebacks, finding none.

Sometimes the fog came down so thick it was necessary to be careful to follow the edge of the stream or lake to keep our bearings and sometimes we came face to face with startled deer. But on clearer days as winter went on, we watched them being fed by the park men. The food truck used to trundle down one of the small roads or riding tracks, the man at the back calling 'oop-oop!' and the deer would run over the fields or down from the forests, following the truck as it described a large circle while supplementary feed was off-loaded. Fallow and red deer together made a large grazing circle.

Seagulls called and screamed their hunger over the Pen Ponds and the ducks were grateful for scraps and bread. The days closed in and the sun seemed to give up, snow threatened. And Owlphonso got ill. In the evening he was perky and playful as ever, but the next morning he refused to eat and looked decidedly droopy.

I called the vet. Owlphonso was still flying around but was lethargic and had a sick look about him. He was given a penicillin, B12 injection. In the afternoon he seemed slightly better but not much. I put him into a cage with a hot water bottle wrapped in thick jumpers, scratched his head and tried to coax him into eating. He still refused, pishing pathetically. I felt helpless. The next morning he was dead.

He was the most charming personality I have ever met or perhaps ever will. He was both amusing and delightful, never aggressive; there was something naively trusting about him. Funny little Owlphonso, my evening companion. I felt sad and a little guilty too : if I'd saved him from a very early death in the market I'd also been a prime factor in his misfortunes. I also could have caused his untimely death by not giving him enough more solid roughage in the shape of feather and fur. Or perhaps he'd picked up a bug, or got a chill when sitting on his top window perch, too near the top window which didn't shut properly. Sadly I buried him under a tree in the garden. His antics, his friendliness, his dawn and late night screeches were sadly missed . . . Alas Owlphonso.

The snow came thick that winter. I thought of skiing but went walking instead with Stinkerbelle who didn't mind it too much. The lakes were covered with sheets of ice and the mallards stood in forlorn groups on the frozen surface. Stinkerbelle explored the ice, finding it strange. She was not used to standing on water and didn't like the experience too much. I was careful to examine her paws every so often in this period to make sure she wasn't getting them cracked or frost bitten. There seemed no sign of this however and no sign of discomfort either. She had warm basin baths in the early morning to which I added a teaspoon of olive oil to keep her webbed paws pliable.

The water course, however, didn't freeze over : even in the coldest,

snowiest weather she would get in for short dips, but I no longer had
to wait heron-like on one foot while she dabbled around under mud
banks or between rushes. Apart from this disinclination to swim for
long periods, however, she was very well acclimatized and my theory
was that if she kept moving and got really dry on her towel before
we bicycled home then there was no reason to believe she might suc-
cumb to any winter ill. I got colds, but Stinkerbelle showed no sign of
being upset by the change of weather.

Then I had another long telephone conversation with Forbes who
by that time had landed up in Suva.

'Look, *bring* her out! I think I've got us a house at last; five acres of
ground, a lovely bush area going down to the sea, perfect! Of course the
house is old and it's horribly expensive but it'll be fine for . . .'

'Any chance of her having a mate as well?'

'Well I've been talking to the appropriate people here and very
kindly they're going to let her in, only she has to have been in England
a *year*. So if you get her a mate, it'll have to have been in England a year
too. I'll send you the instructions for vaccination etc.'

'Then I can just get on a plane with her?'

'No, you'll have to go by sea.'

'By *sea*?' 'You mean by ship and all?'

'Right. You have to come direct from England to Fiji. She mustn't
get off anywhere.'

'You mean five weeks on board with a *nark!*'

'You'll have a lovely holiday, just what you need.'

'Eh? But why does she have to come by *sea*?'

'God knows, they think she might get bitten by a rabid rat or something if she comes by air.'

'*What!*'

'Look, I'll write all the details, just calm down and find out about
shipping companies at your end while I find out more this end, then we
can compare notes and work out the best route.'

The telephone conversation took place about two in the morning
so I was still somewhat fuddled as I shoved Stinkerbelle off my pillow
and went to sleep again.

The next day, fired with optimism, I began ringing shipping lines, trying the big passenger ones first.

'Do you have sailings, London to Fiji?'

'Yes, we do, madam.'

'Would it be possible for me to take the next sailing from London?'

The first was booked up. The second had a berth so I mentioned I wanted to take an otter with me. There was an unbelieving silence. 'A *what*?'

'An otter. Just a little one,' I said, 'She can be in the cabin with me. I mean, she's very clean and house-trained and like a little er – cat really.'

'Oh!' Followed by a giggle at the other end. 'Just a moment.' A query and conversation I felt rather than heard. Then a voice, 'I'm sorry, but it's against all passenger liner regulations to carry animals.'

At the next shipping company the clerk tried hard to convince his superior that Stinkerbelle was adorable, clean, no trouble and could be kept on a lead, but to no avail. 'I'm sorry,' he said and really did sound apologetic, 'but the rules of the company are . . .'

In the afternoon with the help of an agent, I went through a list of cargo freighters sailing in the general direction of Fiji. There were Greek ones, Chinese ones, and all sort of peculiar ones I'd never dreamt of. Some of them took almost two months to get there. Some never did, but ended up in Hamburg or Singapore where I'd have had to change boats. Then finally when I'd almost given up hope : 'Yes, madam, we go to Fiji, and yes, we would take an animal. And yes, we do take a few passengers.'

'How marvellous of you!' I enthused, prepared at that stage to travel as a deck hand on any tatty old Chinese junk. 'When is your next sailing, please?'

'Next month.'

'Great! Well I'll . . .'

'Oh madam, by the way, er, is it yourself wanting the passage with the animal?'

'Why yes, of course!'

'Oh, I'm very sorry, madam, but we don't take *female* passengers.'

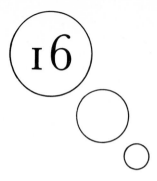

16

More snow and ice : back yard birds fluffed up against the cold waiting for their morning food while chimney smoke thinly wisped into a dour and brooding sky. The roads were thickly plastered, bicycling was out, but I was in one of those moods so I decided the best thing to do was to unravel the Nark, boot her out of bed and take her out for a brisk, exhilarating and very healthy walk, hoping we wouldn't both catch pneumonia on the way.

She seemed fairly indignant that there should be snow lying in *her* garden. She shook her paws in it, got it on her whiskers, sneezed once or twice. It didn't take her long to wake up that morning and soon she began to get into her usual lolloping stride as we continued on to the snowy common, through a crusty forest and down to a small pool there. 'Get in!' I said without much conviction. She stood on it for a couple of minutes, squeaked plaintively, then we lolloped back home.

Mrs Howard was getting in her milk. We talked about the weather and animal problems, and Stinkerbelle went over to be patted, petted and fussed over as usual. She lapped it all up with pitiful moaning little groans; the sort of cries one might expect long-lost-love-lorn-little-Nell-like poor Victorian work-house children to make when finally meeting up with their very own rich fathers and mothers. She enjoyed being fussed over, did Stinkerbelle.

'The pool was solid,' I said.

'Then let her have a swim in my bath,' Mrs Howard said with that immediate kindness of hers.

We hadn't got round to having a bath in our cottage yet. We had a shower but Stinkerbelle didn't like showers.

'Goodness! Really?' I said.

'Yes, you have one too!'

I missed hot baths. I went to get three towels, soap and my loofah. Ten minutes later the Nark was enjoying a bath, fairly luke-warm at this stage, and was showing off in front of us; sinuous dolphining and smooth twists, turns and spins.

After a quarter of an hour of this, I hauled her out and ran in hotter water. Mrs. Howard went off to make some tea and I settled in for a nice peaceful soak.

Two seconds later Stinkerbelle was in again, trying to push me out. She devised a game of chasing an imaginary fish round my feet. Tiring of this, she then decided she would chase her tail, after which she wanted a wrestling match. Water slopped over the sides. I reached over for a towel to mop up with and she dived around behind me and started rooting up the plug I had been firmly sitting on in case of such eventualities.

I managed to get it back in again and deciding enough was enough, threw her out and gave the water a thorough soaping to make it quite clear that it was *my* turn now.

A good loofah down and I was just lying back with my eyes closed when I suddenly realized that *all* the towels were now wet since the Nark was rolling around in the three of them at once. I jumped out dripping, put the least wet one on a high shelf returned to the bath and lay back again.

Another two seconds and there was Stinkerbelle with a roll of toilet paper, batting it over the bathroom floor, getting it thoroughly unrolled and thoroughly mushy. I picked up the squelchy remains, put them next to the towel on the shelf and tried again.

This time it was five seconds of quiet before I realized that why it was quiet was that the Nark had lifted up the seat, got into the toilet and was now dabbling around in the bowl, head first.

At this point I got out in order to plunge her back in the bath and gave her a good wash, then a rinse down.

We both got dry on my one fairly wet towel and I thought how nice it would be to be relieved of the problem and perhaps I would put an advertisement in *The Times* . . . One playful pet otter to temporarily lend excitement to right home, liable to bite children, men and most women, otherwise adorable. No sensible person need apply.

17

But as the winter clouds greyly shuffled and hunched across the London sky one plan after another fell through, mostly because Stinkerbelle's reactions to strangers were getting worse. She seemed to sense, in all those trips out, that I was thinking about the possibilities of leaving her behind. She clung more, stayed between my shoes, never allowed me out of her sight without making a great fuss and, if I as much as left her for five minutes in a strange place, she gave voice to her displeasure and showed her aggressiveness towards all strangers in sight.

Nobody wanted her. 'Put her down!' they said. Simple.

Much more of this, I thought, and I would be going round the nearest bend at a fast trot. I got persecution complexes: martyred by an otter, I told myself. For suddenly I found that I had become 'The Lady with the Otter'. I even got a letter addressed to 'The Lady with . . .', and it opened with, 'Dear Lady with . . .'

The image appeared to be a *fait accompli* and I found to my horror that I was beginning to live up to it. My conversation was generally all otter, my shopping largely otter's, my reading had become otter, animals and behavioural aspects of. My thoughts, my . . . why, I even began to dream about the Nark. Well, perhaps it was better than being addressed as 'Dear Lady with the Boa-Constrictor'.

I probably *smelt* like an otter too. Stinkerbelle had two little scent glands near the base of her tail and when those exuded and I got it on my clothes, the smell did tend to stick around rather. Mind you, it wasn't an unpleasant smell, but to go about redolent of say, lavender water instead, might have met with more appreciation.

And what about Stinkerbelle's image? Generally, it was, 'Oh what a little *darling!*' When she managed to scream at someone or nip though, it was usually, 'Damn, savage, twisted little *monster!*'

Thoughtfully, I turned the letter over in my hands. It invited me to give a talk on Stinkerbelle. But I stared at the heading moodily, 'Dear Lady with the Otter . . . ' However, it ended with 'I wait in hope', so I gave the talk to a group of local church club children and showed them the film of Charlie Brown and Stinkerbelle playing in Bangkok. They enjoyed the amusing scene where parrot Oskar and Nark Stinkerbelle were beak to nose and the scenes of Stinkerbelle swimming in the National Park in Thailand.

I was surprised to find that so many of them had seen Stinkerbelle on her walks, or had heard of her. They were nice children and genuinely intrigued. Later I often met the same children in the park and their interest was a source of delight.

But at home now Stinkerbelle the Nark was trying to push a tomato she had stolen from the fridge under my right foot, which was under the dining-room table. It was not really possible to ignore her but I tried, until I felt a tomato squeezing and oozing over my socks. 'Stinkerbelle, look here! Take it away! No! *Not* in my slippers!' I watched her carry the battered thing off like a footballer, holding it under one arm while lolloping three-footedly over to her water bowl where it was thoroughly sloshed about, juggled with, chased, and batted.

As soon as it was reduced to a messy pulp Stinkerbelle, losing interest, pulled the cardigan off the back of my chair and dragged it off into her pot cupboard. Five minutes later there was an awful sound of crashing china. I had absentmindedly left a half-full teapot standing on a tea-towel, the edge of which had been hanging down over the Nark's knife drawer. The tea towel was now with her *in* the drawer. I spent some time cleaning up bits of china and tea leaves from the floor. I had quite liked that teapot.

And at this point I asked myself *why*? Why, apart from cats, dogs, the occasional guinea pig, bred to be pets and catered for by pet shops, vets and public opinion, why do people keep animals – especially the so-called wild variety? Why does one put up with all the bother, the time, the worry, the criticism, the heartache. *Why* does one put up with it all?

Some people are given an animal, then find themselves stuck with it because they get too fond of their charge to abuse the dependence and trust the animal has come to place in them. Or animals may be rescued from market places and dealers' shops where they are found, sitting sad-eyed, more often than not badly caged, cramped, getting ill or moribund. Some people think it might be fun to have a cute little bear cub in their back yards, while some feel more secure in the midst of their own kind when leading or perhaps being led by a potentially dangerous, large 'pet' annimal.

And sometimes it is the sense of possession, the ambition of the collectors of anything from postage stamps to antiques which leads people to bankrupt themselves in order to add yet another animal to their collection, notwithstanding the fact that they haven't the room for suitable enclosures, the time or the money to ensure and maintain the comfort, well-being and interest of their new item.

What makes a person keep a fox in a small cage, a badger in a tiny concrete compound, monkeys isolated in indoor cages where they go insane with boredom and frustration, pick at their fur and gnaw open wounds on their tails? Why do people keep parrots, or any sort of birds in cages where they cannot fly, sometimes are not even able to stretch their wings, properly preen or sun themselves, or have a showery bath?

Sometimes a collection forms the main interest centre of people's lives; their friends are animal people, there is continual animal talk and perhaps these animal-beings sitting in their little cages form the basis of human relationships. Then there are those who are known to be good with animals and are thus swamped with a collection they don't really want or can't really afford, but haven't the heart to refuse : sick birds and animals of all descriptions are brought to their doorsteps and are rarely turned away. They act as animal casualty officers and the more enlightened release their charges before it's too late to do so.

Yet there are those people who look after their small private collections with solicitude and knowledgeable care : the enclosures they set up for them are large and beautifully adapted to fulfil, as far as possible, those conditions which the natural behaviour of the animal in question needs. Such people in this day and age of shrinking forest and natural landscapes perform an invaluable service in the conservation of wild animals and in the research on behaviour they are able to do.

But besides these aspects of possession, profit, study, hospitality, sympathy, love and so on, there is also this basic human need to be the centre of the universe for some living being – a very great need when one is lonely, or communications for some reason or another between one's fellow men break down or are injured or thwarted in some way. There is this need to give affection and trust and know one will get it back on simple terms which the idiosyncrasies and perhaps the subtle cruelties of our civilized, frustrated, class-confused and aggressive conspecifics do not often allow.

But there is a danger too that one might come to depend on an

124

animal's company too much and therefore retreat into isolation which will but strengthen this dependence.

Then somewhat morosely I thought of those people I considered interesting, genuine, kind and sympathetic enough to prefer to Jacka, Oskar or Stinkerbelle. This list was actually rather short. And there would be no question of choice when I thought of that snarky, bumptious, little type I had met some days before. But good heavens! This was all *wrong!* What *was* I thinking of?

'Stinkerbelle shut up! No, you're not getting anything more to eat now. You're fat enough, for goodness sake.' Where was I? Well yes . . . But one of the most important points in all this is one which any person who has ever kept and had a close relationship with an animal will be able to appreciate; that is the satisfaction, valid in itself since it adds to human understanding, the deep satisfaction one experiences in the company of an animal which contentedly shows a complete trust in one. It is a serenity which reaches back to primordial time and which is finally edifying in itself, for it sets a standard by which to judge the significance of harmony.

Sometimes on a summer morning sitting down by a small pool in the park, oak trees surrounding, deer nearby, squirrels, rabbits, early morning bird song and Stinkerbelle having a half-way rest or a contented roll at my feet after an hour-long exertion of swimming and walking, I felt that real serenity, all too hard to discover amidst the concrete blocks of a polluted city.

One can't discuss things with animals though, and as they trundle along close to the ground, one realizes their basic single-mindedness. They can't describe a scene, converse wittily or in conceptual terms. But on the other hand living with animals and studying their more basic reactions, one comes to more understanding of those mainsprings of one's own more complicated systems.

But this is only a small part of the attempt to answer the question. For the fact that an animal is a living being is necessarily the primary factor engaging one's involvement, whatever the conscious or unconscious roots and motivations of that involvement.

How one treats an animal after that point of engagement will probably describe something of that person's philosophy which may well change in the process.

I admit my attitudes began with the pet outlook, the sympathy, the interest, plus the amusement afforded but soon the feeling of responsibility grew in proportion to my respect for animals as highly individual, emotional and intelligent beings.

One also learns much about people through their attitudes to animals; and it tells one much about people.

'All right, Stinkerbelle, stop thumping at the door! You'll get your snack later.'

I lost the thread of my thoughts so I left it and dashed into the kitchen. Oskar screeched from his perch. Jacka, as soon as she saw Stinkerbelle come in, swooped at her. Stinkerbelle rushed into the pot cupboard and I caged the birds for the night. Stinkerbelle put out her nose, saw it was safe and began fridge bashing.

Five minutes later the parrots were covered up, the Nark was contentedly crunching up a bit of plaice and as I put on my wrestling jumper and braced myself for another energetic and rough-house game with her, I told myself somewhat morosely that if wild animals were to be kept at all, they should be kept in pairs and in semi-captivity only, so that they could communicate with you if they wanted to, but did not have to be dependent on your presence.

'But all right, Stinkerbelle, in the ring!' and I thumped the tail which she'd left poking out of the pot cupboard for that signal purpose. The next minute she'd got my sleeve in her teeth and she was off on a boisterous side-to-side, pull-and-tug, over-and-under spinning-out game and all philosophising and such like was, of necessity, abandoned.

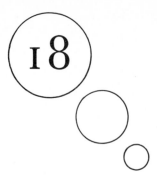

Weeks went by. The world turned and tilted on its axis as buds thick-
ened on the trees, days lengthened and bluer skies promised warmth.
The willows broke out first in a feathery haze of soft greenish-yellow,
while the horse chestnut buds got longer and stickier. It wasn't long
before Stinkerbelle found a frog again. She swam with it downstream,
not holding it with mouth or paws, but tucked in under her chin and
chest as she dog-paddled along.

Spring had grown steadily, delicately across the landscape of the
park; soft, vulnerable-looking bracken shoots had pushed up, un-
curling out of the brown debris of the last year's crop. I saw a blue
heron circle the top Pen Pond and a green woodpecker chatter-
laughed in the forest.

And for Stinkerbelle, it was frogs and frogs again; a fat-bellied
greenish one there, another brown one here. Then in our secluded
forest pool, there was an area of black-spotted, globby jelly. I half
expected her to swim through it, but she didn't. Instead she got so
tail-flippy and excited I wondered if there was an irritant in it. So much
frog glob about made me feel quite optimistic about everything in
general and frogs in particular. After all, frog glob did mean spring
was *really* here.

People seemed to be chirpier too. One day I overheard in the park
as Stinkerbelle was pointed at, 'Oh look! Isn't that *trendy*!' It was a
Saturday, fine, sunny and about three o'clock in the afternoon but I
had decided to take the Nark for an extra afternoon walk because *I*

felt a need to communicate. There had been three or four days of not talking to anyone but the odd shopkeeper, birds and an otter and I was feeling I had better go out in order to do just that . . . communicate with my own kind. I even put on a better coat.

There were plenty of people about enjoying the mild spring weather. My first victims were children. They had left their parents to follow Stinkerbelle upstream. Two little girls, elfin, open-mouthed, plait-types. They were very shy, obviously fascinated and didn't like to ask.

'Do you know what it is?' I said.

'Yes, an otter.'

'That's right!' And as we walked along I treated them to a long dissertation on Stinkerbelle's habit, habitat, type, species and diet.

At the copse end of the stream we parted. A dog owner asked a simple question and went away with an earful of information. I was getting warmed up. Before they could quite open their mouths the next couple received a long lecture. A man, with a dog and child in tow, got a demonstration of Stinkerbelle rolling on her towel and much information about her hunting habits.

The following family had to stand patiently for fully ten minutes while I treated them to a résumé of this otter's life in particular and narks in general.

Thus we lectured our way around the park, leaving a surprised trail of people, wiser in the ways of Stinkerbelle whether they wanted to be wiser or not.

Going home was best though. Bicycling along, Stinkerbelle was leaning sideways, two-thirds of her hanging out of the basket, head up, sniffing the air, sometimes squeaking; a tantalizing sight for anyone in a car behind.

It was a big black smooth-looking job: it followed us slowly for a while. I could almost hear the occupants asking each other, 'What on *earth* is that?' It passed at snail's pace with the two very spruced-up people inside craning their necks to get a better look. It stayed just ahead, still going slow and while the driver peered at us through his rear vision mirror, his mate turned round to stare through the back window.

At the the bend on the road there was a sudden, violent screech of brakes and a simply awful swerve as an oncoming Mini with nice leap-frog effect jumped the grass verge before bounding back on to the road. The car in front stopped, and the Mini driver got out raising his fists.

The large car owner was looking rather put out. Stinkerbelle squeaked and waved her paws as we sailed past. Then I noticed another car swing round the bend and almost crash into the Mini's backside.

'Well, well!' I said as I bicycled on, patting her on her head, 'Stinkerbelle my Nark, we've communicated!'

19

Stinkerbelle, Stinker*belle*, *Stinkerbelle*, Stinkerbelle-the-Nark, Stinker-belle-the-*Nark!*

I first heard of the place through the complex otter vine. Why I hadn't heard of it before nobody knew. They thought I did know about it and had tried it: it was a very small zoo, not listed in my zoo book. It was half an hour train ride from my nearest station and it had two otters.

I telephoned immediately.

'Yes, two males.'

'Oh er – what kind are they?'

'One *lutra*, Indian smooth and one short-clawed Asian.'

Male, short-clawed Asian! I couldn't believe it. 'But that's like Stinkerbelle, I mean I have a . . . And I'm . . . ' I got a little incoherent before it was agreed that I should go out and see him that very after-noon. He sounded pleased too at the prospect of getting a mate for his little Olly as he called him.

'Okay, Stinkerbelle!' I said as I put some fish in her ice bucket. 'There you are, feed yourself when you feel like it and don't bat the ice under the fridge. I'm off on an advance recce prospecting your chances.'

I found the zoo a charming little place, Dave, the owner giving the animals very personal attention. The otter enclosure was large, oval in shape and had a narrow swimming moat surrounding its periphery. A chain-link fence with an overhang went up from the moat's edge. The water was circulated by pump, and a rockery with pools interrupted the moat at one point. A huge and ancient oak stood in the enclosure and between its roots were deep burrows which the otters obviously used as a holt. They had a small sleeping hutch as well.

We went into the enclosure through a small gate, crossed the moat on a plank and Dave called the otters. At the call, two heads appeared at an opening between the large oak roots.

The first was a fairly large head with shortish whiskers, a sedate looking face with an inquiring expression; this was Gary, the Indian *lutra*'s face. Then out over the top of him, pranced little Olly – a real amblonyx; something critical, inquisitive and busy-body in the quicker movement and the rather indignant expression as he bounded over in all haste to see what was up. He was followed, at a more lollopy big-pawed pace, by Indian Smooth Gary who was about two and a half times Olly's size.

It was like seeing the otter equivalent of Laurel and Hardy. But that comparison won't really do, for Gary was a beautiful animal, long and lithe in movement, big claws on paddy paws, a wider, bigger head, chocolate-brown colour and buff underneath, especially under the chin area.

Olly was smaller than Stinkerbelle, being much younger; he was about eighteen months old, Dave informed me, whereas Stinkerbelle was almost five and a half. He hadn't quite her ashy tinge, nor was he so white under the chin.

His tail was only half the size too at the base; she was very broad across the beam was Stinkerbelle. He had lovely long whiskers though and was very lively. They were both tame and would allow anyone to pat and play with them. But soon they lost interest in us, dived into the moat for a swim, then got out to have a wrestling-chasing game on the bank. Olly-the-small was more bouncy than Gary-the-large who had a more sinuous power-in-reserve style.

I was thrilled to see otters kept in such good ottery conditions, otters which were obviously happy and content with their lot. Dave and I decided that I should bring Stinkerbelle out as soon as I possibly could for a trial with his two.

132

A few days later, I conned the Nark into her travelling cage and covered it over with a blanket. I'd decided I wouldn't lead her into a strange otter's territory this time but carry her in in her cage before uncovering it as I thought she might not have yet got over her other wildlife park experience. She had had nightmares for a week after that episode, jerking and groaning in her sleep, quite different from her drinking dreams. Sometimes she would have a drinking dream during which her half-closed mouth would go gulp-gulp-gulp in my ear waking me up and sending me out for her water bowl, because I couldn't sleep through such a noise. I used to dig her in the ribs, she would wake up, pip, put her head in the bowl and really drink, then we could all go back to sleep again.

As I was saying, I didn't want her jerking, shuddering and groaning around my ankles, my neck or sort of wrapped round my head, all of which happened after that wild-life park business. Besides which, both otters might have felt disinclined to love her, or have taken umbrage at her presence, in which case she could dash back into her very own territory, i.e. her sleeping travelling cage.

So we carried it in across the moat and with Stinkerbelle squeaking inside put it down centre. Gary and Olly couldn't contain their excited curiosity as I unlatched the door.

Jean, the otter keeper, held the two males back as Stinkerbelle emerged, wary and humped-up looking. I held my breath and got ready to grab, but she got between my feet, twisting around between them to keep nose to nose to both Gary and Olly who were excitedly circling her.

I stroked and talked to her as the circling went on, Stinkerbelle defensive, the males intent. There was no animosity, but as soon as I stood on one foot she immediately rushed away to get herself wedged between Jean's shoes. She showed no signs of hostility towards Jean and indeed was now looking to her for protection. Stinkerbelle obviously didn't quite trust my feet any more. We all talked to her, making consoling and encouraging noises. Then Jean patted and stroked her.

'Do be a bit careful as yet,' I warned.

'Oh she'll be all right, she's lovely. There!' and Stinkerbelle responded with her lapping-it-up-moans, asking for more petting and consolation, and began to sound like a cat-with-gripes. You couldn't imagine a more pathetic little creature! Naturally enough the males, getting bored with this, soon flipped off for a short swim and another racing game. Dave's wife then came into the enclosure to pat Stinkerbelle and to tell her how beautiful she was.

Stinkerbelle was behaving herself incredibly well with strange humans, responding to the kindness in their voices. I wasn't too surprised though, for she usually did respond well to women's voices cooing at and making a fuss over her with affection and sympathy. But I was truly delighted at the way they were all getting on with one another. Jean said how lucky they were to have a female for Olly at last.

Then the males bounded over again. We eased Stinkerbelle out from between our feet as the big circling-feinting process went on. Stinkerbelle got sniffed both ends at once and although she didn't seem to like the experience over much, rolled over on to her side submissively, got nosed over by both of them, but showed very little sign of distress; there was no trembling or shivering. She seemed to be putting up with it, going through the polite codes of submission. She wasn't looking very impressed with her intended though and as they withdrew she took off, ignoring them, sour, prim-faced and just a little worried, exploring the new domain.

She obviously wanted to get in and swim but couldn't make the decision to go down the fairly steep side and into water without knowing how deep it might be. Instead, she plumped for one of the rockery pools, swirled round in it and was joined at once by the two males. This time, she hesitantly nosed Olly back. Then she went off on another recce, examined their sleeping quarters and had a spraint in her tray followed by large *lutra* Gary sprainting all over it and then Olly who was neater.

She was still overwhelmed every time they showed her too much attention, but she was getting bolder, now following the others more closely. She even responded to an overture to play until, as if overcome by her own audacity, she rushed back to lie between Jean's feet.

134

Jean was stroking her as the males bounded up all vim and vigour, wanting to nudge her out. It was too much for Stinkerbelle, but instead of snapping at them, the Nark snapped at Jean – a puncture bite on the hand. I apologized feelingly, but Jean, stroking Stinkerbelle again was calming everyone down and saying it didn't matter at all.

The bite seemed a displacement one. Stinkerbelle had hitherto shown no sign of aggression or hostility and at the end of another hour was still very attracted to Jean's feet whenever she felt insecure or felt like being stroked and talked to.

So finally we all parted, promising to come back the following week. I hoped by that time the large fibre-glass pool which I'd ordered would have arrived. I felt very optimistic about the outcome. Under such good conditions, with kind, sympathetic people, good diet and mate it *must* work!

That evening I got a call from Dave: his two otters hadn't stopped trying to find Stinkerbelle since she had left. Gary the *lutra* had been carrying one of the small covers I'd left behind around with him and was continually searching her traces. Besides this, Olly had been screaming his head off. They weren't interested in food and Dave had been having one hell of a time with them so would I mind if I brought her out for good and all next time please.

He sounded somewhat distraught and I thought I could hear otters in the background. I understood his problem and agreed to take her out as soon as the pool arrived. I'd stay a few days and nights to help with the odds and ends, putting in the pool, settling her down, then I would start tailing off my presence until . . .

We went for extra long walks in the park that week. I was waiting for a call from Dave to tell me that the pool had arrived when suddenly Stinkerbelle came on heat, turning her again from a docile, home-loving, game-playing Nark, into a jumpy, digging, continual pip-squeaking, never still bag of nervous energy. I checked her heat-boards along the fence, the stones at the bottom and got ready to perform nifty things with my feet at the door. She never got snappy, or aggressive in these times for as usual, she seemed to know she couldn't help it.

135

At the end of the first day I said, 'Oh well, Stinkerbelle, tomorrow you'll be all right,' for often these heat periods only lasted a day or two. But by the end of the exhausting second day, after I'd failed to tire her out in the park and found her balancing on the top room's window-sill looking ready to jump, I decided to take her out to her two boyfriends because this seemed to be a big heat.

It happened about the same time the year before and went on for a week. I believed it was not a seasonal thing, but was triggered off by certain circumstances. Perhaps her meeting with two eager males had given her the idea and set her hormones in action.

I telephoned Dave and early the next morning, my neighbour, generously helpful as usual, drove us bag and baggage out to the zoo.

Stinkerbelle was still very much a nark-en-oestrus extremis. In a way I was glad. I hadn't had time to take her on a last, long, sentimental walk through the park, or have her clinging desperately to me. She didn't cling in this state. Her independent mood was making it easier for me too.

I led her in, then took off her harness and lead. Gary and Olly couldn't believe their good luck! Stinkerbelle was surrounded and this time there was no submissiveness about her: a sudden, squeaky snap warned both of them off. For a moment I thought she would really bite Gary-the-large, advancing on him with flattened ears and mean expression. I picked her up fast and we all dispersed to calm down for a while.

On the grass again, she got between my feet, but didn't stay there for long; Stinkerbelle in this state seemed quite sure about her powers over male otters. They circled her slowly, carefully, until little Olly hugged her rear end, paws encircling her haunches. The embrace didn't please her, however, for she turned her head over her back and gave him such a hard look that he let go at once, then off she galloped closely followed by her two fascinated suitors.

As soon as they caught up with her, she bossily chased Gary the large *lutra* away, but allowed Olly to nudge and sniff her. Five minutes later the *lutra* returned, wanting to be friendly, but she faced him tense and resentful, her attitude making it quite clear that as far as she was concerned, three was a crowd. The *lutra* looked disconsolate for a moment, but soon bounded away to the moat, swam and played – all the while calling them to come and join him.

They didn't respond, for now they had begun to play together. Gary came back eager to participate, but this time Stinkerbelle attack-screamed at him, forcing him back once more. Little Olly, feeling his affection torn for a moment, got between them, nudging Stinkerbelle back as if trying to protect his big friend. Then the two short-clawed otters ran off together. Olly tried to mate her and she let him hug her a few times before rather irritably shaking him off, for she wanted to explore the edge of the moat. Olly followed still trying to cling to her.

She was very lively, seeming to find the situation immensely satisfying, and when Gary bounded up again she at last agreed to let him play with them. She was beginning to demand attention, obedience, affection, play, and whatever else female amblonyx on heat might demand. She got it too, from both of them as she led them around their enclosure. The two males had a slightly hang-doggy look about them and were careful to let her have her own way in all things.

It took her only about half an hour this time to brave the moat and soon the three of them were chasing one another, swimming round and round or having vigorous tussling, wrestling matches. It was a true triangular mix-up, although every now and then she would squeak Gary off and the two-of-a-kind would chase him across the enclosure before turning back to their own fun and games.

Their acceptance of one another truly amazed me. I felt a great relief, for here she was, not taking the slightest notice of me, not even responding to my call. Indeed, I might never have existed! She had eyes only for her two consorts, especially Olly and she was obviously well pleased with her role in the new situation.

'It *will* work' we all exclaimed happily as we left the enclosure. Dave then told me that the pool had arrived; a big triangular-shaped one with a deep circular pool in the middle and raised shelves along the sides and towards the pointed end. Three otters could have a lovely time swirling in such a space.

When I got back to the enclosure a boisterous game was in progress,

for Stinkerbelle, having decided that Gary was too much of an interesting playmate to chase off, had allowed him to join in a friendly, but
fiercely energetic tumbling during which Olly was continually trying
to mate her with a look of serious determination on his whiskery little
face. I hoped he was mature enough at eighteen months.

We put in a new sleeping shed for them. A load of hay went into it
together with Stinkerbelle's dog basket and covers. Jean also brought
a door mat for drying themselves on, placing it outside the door. The
otters could hardly contain their curiosity and as soon as we'd finished
went in to inspect it. Olly carried some straw into Stinkerbelle's basket
to make it more homely before sharing it with her; Gary chose a low,
straw-covered shelf to stretch himself out on and for a while they all
rested.

Dave then brought a collection of big willow logs and paving stones
and we set the pool in. I was very appreciative of the way everyone
helped. We also made a sand-earth digging place and surrounded it
with logs. By the time all this work was finished it was rather late and
time for the otters' evening meal.

We threw fish over the fence to disperse the three of them before
Jean and I went in with the food trays. Everything worked well until
suddenly Stinkerbelle looked up, left her food, followed Jean and bit
her on the leg with a sharp attack screech. I pulled the Nark off, then
followed Jean out. Meanwhile, Stinkerbelle went on crunching up her
fish with complete indifference.

Jean was having her leg bandaged. There were four small triangular
cut-outs and fairly deep. 'I'm terribly sorry!' I began.

'Look it's all right, quite all right,' she said. 'She'll be better in a
few days. She just has to settle down.'

'I do hope so but . . . '

'I won't feed them for a day or two because of my leg,' Jean said.
'Then we'll try again.'

Such big-heartedness towards the little savage made me feel even
more apologetic and very worried. Obviously someone had to start
some time going in to feed her and trying to communicate, but I could
see that it was not going to be easy.

138

The next morning, however, Dave informed us that the three otters had slept curled up together in Stinkerbelle's basket. I was very pleased about this. Dave had been in with them, fed them and there had been no untoward incident.

We watched the three of them playing together. Gary had obviously won Stinkerbelle's heart with his charm and big-hearted friendliness. In fact, he couldn't get away from her and after they'd fed, I watched in amazement as Stinkerbelle, spurning little Olly, her own species, tried in every possible way to seduce the much bigger *lutra*. He lay on his back and mouthed at her playfully, or patted his big paws at her while she lay on top of him, flat out, spread-eagled on his stomach as she slowly sniffed over his face or nudged his neck. I was reminded of early cinema sirens.

Then she turned and sniffed his tail before swivelling slowly around on his stomach again, gently mouthing his neck as she rubbed herself against him. It was all highly romantic and she had a gentle, rather impatient, flirtatious and demanding look about her, while large Gary lay there, letting her nudge and sniff him and generally carry on like a well-experienced courtesan. Being quite a different species naturally he made no attempt to mate her. This however seemed to make Stinkerbelle more determined than ever to seduce him.

It did my heart good to see such affection. 'Only for goodness sake, Stinkerbelle!' I felt like shouting at her from the sidelines, 'it's the wrong species!' Olly, however, was there too and while Stinkerbelle was occupied in caressing Gary around the neck, purposeful little Olly was hugging her aft and really attempting some serious mating.

During the day we watched them. The pool was a great success, the three of them spinning, diving, dolphining, churning up the water, chasing one another round and round. Stinkerbelle made for Gary, Olly chased Stinkerbelle, then down into the moat they'd splash and back again.

When they tired of this, the three of them rolled in the grass, dug in their sandpit or went to scuffle around in their shed. Olly's face would appear for an instant. Peace for a few minutes, then Gary's face would peer out to see that all was well. Little Olly would take more straw and stuff it into Stinkerbelle's basket. Then all would be quiet for an hour or so.

That evening Dave said he would feed them again to see how he got on. I stood back and watched as he did so. Food trays were placed with nary a nip. 'There you are,' said Dave, pleased too. 'She'll be all right.'

And suddenly I felt that it *would* be all right. At last, Stinkerbelle was going to be content and sooner or later have cubs and the people who were looking after her were happy to have her and would look after her very well indeed.

That night Jean, her husband and I, went to their local and celebrated the outcome.

The next morning Dave said he'd been in again and had no trouble, Stinkerbelle had ignored him. All was well. I saw the otters in the moat, went over and came across a most amazing sight. There was Stinkerbelle somehow spread-out in the water, looking as though she'd got her specific gravity all wrong or had become twice as buoyant as she ought to have been. She wasn't swimming or making any swimming movements whatsoever, yet her head was up, her back paws were trailing, her front ones relaxed in the water and her tail twisting just a fraction. In this manner she was cruising along the moat at quite a speed. About six inches from her tail, little Olly was keeping pace like some page boy intent on doing his duty.

'But what on earth?' I began. Then all at once, just in front of Stinkerbelle's head, rose Gary's. It came out of the water, took a big gulp of air and submerged, while Stinkerbelle-Cleo went gliding on. 'Good God, she's riding on his back!' I cried, following them round. Gary came right up then in a humpy-dolphin movement and made as if to get out. Stinkerbelle, however, was enjoying the ride so much that she nipped his neck, so great-hearted Gary carried her on, swimming under water most of the time.

When Gary got tired of continually circling the moat, he eased her off his back and bounded off to the pool before she could pull him back again. Here he started to swirl with her while Olly, always awake to opportunity and still in the water, hugged her stern. This she

140

tolerated absentmindedly, being far too interested in seducing Gary.

It was a very peculiar situation to say the least, and for mating purposes not one which one might have called ideal. Gary no doubt took her fancy as he was larger and more mature than Olly, but of course he made no attempt to do what Olly was up to. So as far as Stinkerbelle was concerned, it was a matter of Love's Labour's Lost. On the other hand she was so occupied up front as it were, that she was a bit careless about what Olly was up to at the other end. I wasn't sure that one could expect cubs from this performance though, as I believe most mustelidae take some time to actually mate and Olly was mostly interrupted, for whenever Gary moved, Stinkerbelle followed him.

But by evening I was still pleased with their acceptance of one another and the harmony between them.

My neighbour had driven out to collect me and half my baggage, as Dave had suggested that on the morrow, Sunday, he would feed the otters and on early Monday morning I would come out again for I planned to take the train out every day for a few days, then every two days, three days, a week and so on, tailing off during a two or three-week period. When we left, with mutual congratulations, Stinkerbelle was happily leaping around with Gary and Olly in an early evening game and hardly bothered to respond to my call.

It was very quiet at hope: I kept expecting Stinkerbelle to drape a paw out of her drawer, or come sliding out of the pot cupboard, or out of my bed. I found a peanut and a button in my shoe when I went to put it on. But the relief at the happy outcome was greater than the regret : there she was, really content with two marvellous otters dancing in attendance, kind, knowledgeable people looking after her and she'd been too distracted to respond when I'd said good-bye to her.

I had a long refreshing shower, made some tea and, with a parrot on each shoulder, took to bed, settling down with a book and saying to myself, 'Well, tomorrow, I can . . . Yes . . . I don't have to . . . I can even sleep in! And then maybe I'll go to the Tate or the National and take my time and later, yes, I might even go to the cinema, get my plane ticket organized, and cable my friends, who after home leave and travel ought to be back in Bangkok by now'. Then I convinced myself that I was very pleased she was so content that she didn't miss me. She hadn't even noticed when I left her! And so on, feeling somewhat bereft at not having an otter bouncing round my feet and yet so relieved at knowing she was settled at last and so satisfactorily. Jacka and Oskar had a feed on the table and flew over to perch for the night on the bed head.

And I was just going to turn off the light at eleven p.m. when the telephone rang.

I bounded downstairs. Perhaps it was Forbes and I could tell him the good news! I picked up the receiver. 'Hello!' eagerly.

'Hello.' It was Dave's wife.

'Yes?'

'Will you please take your otter away immediately!'

'What? Er – pardon?'

The voice at the other end was obviously very upset – which made two of us. Dave's wife worked during the day, so I hadn't had too much contact with her, but whenever I had met her she had been very charming and she had petted and stroked Stinkerbelle and had said how lovely she was. So I understood that something awful must have happened.

'But what's wrong?'

'She's bitten Dave!'

'No! When?'

'This evening.'

'But they'd been fed! Did he . . . ?'

'He went in to rescue a chicken which was drowning in the moat and she attacked him.'

'Oh I . . . I'm terribly sorry! Of course I'll . . . ' By this time we had both calmed down and she was very nice about it, but quite firm that I should come as soon as possible to take her away. 'His leg is bitten, she tore his sandals, his shirt, his trousers and his thumb,' she explained. 'And we just can't let Jean ever go near her or go in to feed her. Why your otter could attack her too! She went for Dave in front of visitors, screamed at him as well. Jean was watching. We just can't have it! I

142

mean Jean goes in and *plays* with our otters and visitors like to see it, but now yours screams at everyone it sees. We just can't . . . '

'Tonight is rather late,' I said. 'Would tomorrow morning very early be all right?'

'Yes, we'll see you tomorrow then.'

And after a few more apologies and commiserations we rang off.

I had a glassful of old whisky which had been lying around the house for six months or more and didn't think of anything very much.

The next morning my neighbour kindly came to the rescue again with offers of transport.

I could hear Stinkerbelle as soon as we got out of the car. A real attack scream. Nearer, and I saw Dave on the far side of the enclosure but quite a distance from it; he was feeding his fine collection of woolly monkeys. Stinkerbelle was still attack screaming in his direction.

Dave was apologetic. 'Look I'd love to go on with it, but we can't have her going on like this. Visitors today and she screams at them all.'

'I'm terribly sorry about your leg and your thumb,' I said and through the noise of the Nark still screaming her head off said again how sorry I was and if he wouldn't mind, could I feed her before taking her as she was probably hungry which was making her worse.

'Be careful about going in,' he warned, 'She can't be trusted with anyone.'

I fed her and quietened her down. She didn't eat very much, but I noticed a difference in her attitude to the other otters immediately. She was not demanding attention anymore. She played with them, but half-heartedly. She looked thoroughly peevish and fed up. The love affair was obviously over. Then she screamed at some zoo visitors who had just arrived, so I hurriedly picked her up, put her lead on, said farewell to Gary and Olly and took her out.

She clung to me, moaning: the pathetic act. Stinkerbelle the Nark having had her romantic holiday now wanted home. Of course she was no longer on heat.

We did a quick pack-up, good-byes to the zoo people, mutual apologies and commiserations again and there we were, driving back with the Nark exhausted, curled up on my lap making moans and

143

squeaks every time she could work up the energy to do so, which actually was most of the time.

Once inside the house she suddenly relaxed, then took off, sniffing all over the back garden, her shed, her pot cupboard, her drawer, her bathroom bit, making sure all her usual places were still there. I dunked her thoroughly in a bucket of warm water, put some ointment on one toe which she'd cut and off she galloped upstairs and into my bed, where she promptly passed out.

My neighbour and her sister came in and we all downed beers and muttered consolations at one another in fairly subdued tones. I was glad that I hadn't sent a cancelling cable to Thailand concerning a male otter.

But I began to feel ridiculous again. I mean, I'd sooner die than visit my doctor because when I thought Stinkerbelle was going to be settled, I had all my vaccinations and told him stories about how I was off to the other side of the world. Let's hope I stay healthy, I thought, as I called her down, fed her and after all this collapsed for the afternoon with, round my head in semicircular and contented drape, Stinkerbelle the Nark.

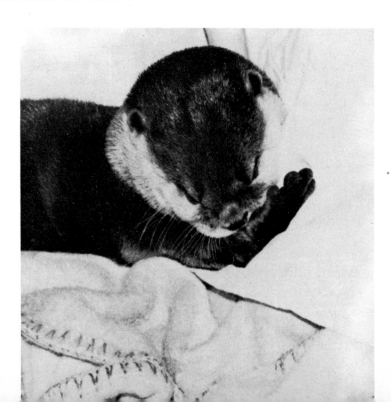

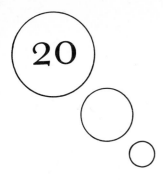

20

After our little zoo episode Stinkerbelle was very reluctant to let me out of her sight. Even asleep she had to be curled round my head or feet, and if she slept on the covered arm-chair, she had to have one of my wrists to put her paws round. She also didn't like to walk too far in the park. And although this might have been due to the hotter weather I was more inclined to believe, puffing after her as she galloped down the home straight towards the bicycle where she stood up waiting to be lifted into the basket, I was more inclined to the belief that she wanted to be quite sure she was going back to her very own garden, her very own pot cupboard and her very own knife drawer. There was nothing more calculated to make me feel unpleasant than trying to elsewhere establish, albeit happily, a creature which was, except in heated moments, so trustful of me, so attached and dependent on my return of affection.

I had tried to work out why it all went wrong at the little zoo: evidently, the sight of Dave running across the enclosure to rescue a chicken from the moat must have aroused her aggressiveness. He was, after all, still virtually a stranger to her. But I believe I should have stayed out there at least a month, going in with the keeper concerned, either Dave or Jean, and slowly over that period, made quite sure of her acceptance of them. I ought not to have been so pleased and re-lieved at the way in which she *seemed* to have accepted them.

Perhaps during her heat period she tolerated everyone because she had other more important things on her mind. And no doubt I had been too impressed by the relationship between the otters themselves to think more deeply about the otter-human relationship.

Had the fact that she'd been mated made her that much more aggressive? Or was it more likely to be a tendency, growing stronger as she got older. 'For goodness sake, what am I going to *do* with you, Stinkerbelle?' I asked her, but she didn't respond because she was asleep and snoring with her paws clasped round my feet as I read a letter from Forbes who had been promised a six-week leave in the near future.

We had had a serious discussion over the telephone as to whether or not the best thing would be to put her down. Emotionally, I couldn't countenance this 'solution'. Objectively, it might have meant the only release for all of us; this was taking into account the way her aggressiveness was developing towards strangers and the way she attack screamed at them. No ordinary zoo would take an animal which would carry on so at their visitors and surely no private person could be found who would give her a home and undertake the responsibility involved. If she were to be subjected to cruel isolated conditions, then wouldn't it be better . . .

I'd look at her playing round my feet, or watch her swimming, enjoying herself in the park, experience the way she had such absolute trust in me; it was a decision I just could not make.

Then a few weeks after the little zoo episode, I noticed Stinkerbelle looked fatter than usual. I took her for extra long walks and cut down her food intake. It made no difference. About a month had gone by and her four nipples were still very red, somewhat enlarged and they stayed that way. This usually happened when she was on heat but the phenomenon was temporary.

My neighbour came in to inspect her as well. 'You know I do believe she could be,' she said. 'She does look a bit bulky in the cub carrying area.' We both watched her and wondered. Was she? Was she indeed having cubs?

She seemed to be doing a lot of frantic nest-building too. Usually she would take newspapers, covers or anything else she could find into her pot cupboard or drawer, but this activity seemed now to engage

146

her for much longer periods and she was much more purposeful about it. She was making nests all over the house; under chairs, under beds, behind wardrobes, behind the stove and so on.

To a large extent, she also gave up playing with me: she would play gentle games for a while, but there were no more very energetic wrestling matches, no more tail-slapping games. She played more sedately and often ignored an invitation to a game, wanting to be groomed and stroked instead. If she's having cubs, I thought, then whatever anyone says there's no question of any drastic measures being taken.

Forbes was due back in another month and I finished the letter, 'so if she is, and we can settle her, then she *must* have a mate.'

After this I sent a long explanatory cable to my friends who by this time had arrived back in Bangkok. The reply came back: 'Young male located. Documents following.'

The news was heartening. 'Stinkerbelle Nark old thing, your mate's on his way! And maybe, I mean if you have a mate and cubs, you'll settle down and we can find someone to love and look after you all when we organize a suitable enclosure.' I was very optimistic.

Two weeks later, optimism was tinged with excitement for the documents arrived. Another cable came and finally there he was at the airport in a wire-fronted plywood box.

Understandably, he was still frightened and valiantly snorted when I peered in at him. I had the ice bucket with me with small bits of fish and meat in it. First though, I poured water into a container tied up near the front section. He came forward to drink thirstily and stayed there to have water trickled over his nose. I pushed a little fish at him through the bars. He came at it with a loud spit-snort to scare me off but took it gently enough out of my fingers, sitting back in his cage to eat it. He was hungry, yet hadn't made that ear splitting snarl-squeak, get-off-it noise otters generally make when grabbing food.

He kept taking fish from my fingers until I considered that was enough for a start. He was still frightened, but the food had calmed him.

'Well,' I said to the airport vet when he arrived, 'he is certainly lively enough, he's eating, he's truly an amblonyx and of course I accept delivery.'

At home, Stinkerbelle had been left partitioned off upstairs with all her accoutrements. I dashed up, shoved some fish at her to keep her happy, then dashed down again to the garden where the box had been deposited on the lawn.

I had decided to call the new little otter Chanok after a character in the Thai Ramakien.

The garden shed had been prepared for him with Stinkerbelle's travelling-sleeping cage in one corner covered over with felt and stuffed with old woollens. It was dark and cosy in the cage. A spraint tray, placed in the other corner and surrounded with bricks, was tilted at one end for I hoped he'd stand on the brick surround when sprainting into it. A plastic sheet had been spread over the floor and on top, felt matting and towels. Near this was put a big plastic bowl filled with water and his eating and drinking tray.

The shed had a window which let in plenty of light even if the door were closed, but I had a sheet of plywood jammed across the open doorway which left the top half free for me to peer over. I put a good dollop of spraint from his tray into his new one and hoped I'd remember not to use that particular old dessertspoon ever again. When all this was done, we brought out a little fish and meat, put it into his food bowl, put his opened box into the shed, jammed in the ply, stood back and waited.

It didn't take him long to smell the food. Surprisingly, he said Hah! to it before getting down to the munching process. After the third piece, however, remembering he was on strange territory, he started to explore; he sniffed at the spraint tray, contemplated it, drew back, sniffed again, then stood on the bricks and sprainted.

He said, Hah! softly and warily to Stinkerbelle's cage, got half way in and backed out fast before impulsively diving in again. Very quietly, I began lifting out his own box, but he heard me and came rushing out of the sleeping cage with a frightened snort.

'All right,' I said, 'here!' and gingerly held a piece of fish down to him over the ply. The gentle way in which he took it from my fingers showed that he was used to being hand fed and that, as my kind friends in Bangkok wrote, had probably been in captivity for some time.

That he was not quite out of the cub stage was clear, but one of the first things I had noticed when he had emerged from his box was the fact that he had an inch-wide, irregular line of fur missing across his back; the brown guard hairs had gone from this line leaving the pale, whitish under-fur exposed. And the next thing I saw was a big round mark above his left shoulder, a lot of fur was missing here and there was a scab about the size of a ten pence piece in the centre of it. On the underside of this shoulder was another small patch of missing fur.

I came to the sad conclusion that they were probably trap wounds. Otters in the Bangkok market or dealers' shops often have damaged paws, or worse. Chanok had probably been jammed by some vicious bit of iron across his back and jabbed in the side. He must have been very young when caught for he still had fur which stuck up, rather like

149

puppy fur. It wasn't very thick either. He was probably only about nine months old.

Apart from his old injuries, however, he seemed in good health; bright eyes, lively, alert and quick of movement; and, most importantly, his spraint showed no signs of diarrhoea. I wanted to look at him more closely though, so that afternoon when he'd recovered from travel fatigue and was ready for another meal I hoisted myself over the ply and sat down on the shed floor with a plate of food. It was very quiet; no movement from the cage, no sign of Chanok. Worriedly, I put my head in the cage and almost landed back in the spraint tray as he snorted me out. 'All right!' I said irritably composing myself, and out he came again, saying 'Hah!' expecting food.

I kept very still. He came up to my lap, sniffed, got bolder, nosed up to my fingers, neatly took a piece of eel and sat with one paw on my knees to eat it. He was obviously used to people and although any untoward movement scared him, he certainly knew that fingers gave fish.

After he'd eaten, he settled down to groom himself. I tried to touch him and scratch his back a little. It was evident he had fleas and was very dirty; his under chin, neck and chest areas which ought to have been white and light grey were instead a dirty yellowish-brown. As soon as he saw my hand approaching, or felt one finger touch him though, he'd leap around with a frightened and defensive snort, tensing up, head drawn back. It was interesting, that while half-way up on my lap taking food from my fingers he was so gentle and un-afraid, but once my fingers went away from my lap and travelled towards him, he immediately thought they were some dangerous animal.

He looked comically fierce at these moments and I took it carefully, letting my hands drift off to my lap then down to the floor keeping them there for him to sniff at and all the time making encouraging sounds. I coaxed him out again with the last piece of fish, talked to him for an hour or so then left him to rest again.

For the next meal, besides some vitaminized meat and eel, I took out several large pieces of plaice as I wanted to tempt him into the

150

big bowl of water to get some of the dirt off. Also, I wanted to see what sort of damage was under that nasty looking scab. I let him sniff the first chunk then threw it in the bowl into which I'd put luke warm water.

With some hesitation he got his head, neck and front paws under water to reach for it but just after fishing out the third piece his front half was nicely soaked. It was then I discovered a horrible-looking, running sore under the scab; a greenish-yellow weeping mess which would necessitate treatment. A cleaning out and stitching up process by a vet was needed. Not a happy prospect.

But he was getting used to me, and that evening I was able to really touch him for the first time. It's amazing how much of a thrill it gives one to win an animal's confidence. The following day I scratched his back while he was busy scratching his front and from then on whenever he groomed himself I was able to groom him at the same time without his snorting or trying to bite. He was very independent though and would allow me to finger groom him only when he was engaged in grooming himself for in this way he could pretend that he was not giving in to any solicitations.

I'd sent off two lots of spraint to a laboratory, labelled Stinker-belle's and Chanok's, and they'd both come back negative, so that if it hadn't been for Chanok's suppurating wound I could have started getting the two otters acquainted. As it was, we made a trip to a very helpful vet in the country.

Chanok was duly put out. The wound area was shaved and the whole thing was cleaned out, a drainage tube inserted and his skin neatly stitched together again. Antibiotics and powder were pre-scribed and no swimming for about ten days. 'He'll probably get his own stitches out,' said the vet. 'Anyway ring me after ten days to tell me how he's making out.' We had also given him a good sprinkling of flea powder to rid him of those parasites.

At home I took all his rugs, covers and towels out of the shed and spread a clean sheet over the felt and lino on the floor. A couple of freshly laundered towels and a clean blanket went into his sleeping box. We put him down to rest and slowly but surely he came to. By

evening he wanted a meal. The experience hadn't made him more frightened, put back the taming process or diminished his appetite. I was confident that his wound would now heal and in this respect I was well satisfied.

The trouble was, that until it did heal, Stinkerbelle had to be kept out of the back garden and away from him. As long as Stinkerbelle didn't think she was being kept out, everything was fine. I didn't want her tearing his drainage tube, or grooming his stitches out, so I took her for two walks a day and I had to eat twice as much to keep myself from getting thinner whilst wearing off her energy. Because Stinkerbelle couldn't have her back garden, she demanded the whole of the rest of the property in compensation which meant having to remember to put front room pot plants out of reach, chairs away from tables and ink bottles off the dining room one. When she was not chewing at the dog hole, or batting, or pulling at it with high squeaky what-the-hell! sounds, she was demanding extra attention, food and generally giving me an ear-full.

What she was still not demanding though and hadn't been since her romantic interlude were those rough wrestling matches and I kept asking myself, was she, or was she not having cubs?

The gestation period was probably three months. Two and a half had passed 'Well, Stinkerbelle,' I told her as she lay fatly on the kitchen floor, 'if you aren't having cubs, it's short rations with no seconds for months afterwards, so you'd better produce!'

Meanwhile Chanok was thriving, his wound healing nicely. He was allowed out in the back garden to play and enjoyed it. He was also letting me scratch his back more and more and forgetting to leap like a dervish every time I made an untoward movement. In fact I was so wrapped up in otter activity during this time that I was fast developing a tendency to say 'Hah!' to everyone instead of 'Hello.'

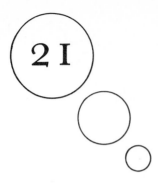

21

Before Stinkerbelle met her new mate I fed them both in their respective territories: Stinkerbelle in the kitchen, Chanok in his shed. He was at the stage of playing with me and there were very few snorts in the process. After they had both eaten and drunk and groomed themselves, I considered we were all ready to communicate; besides, Stinkerbelle was already tugging at the dog hole.

I left the shed door open and went back to the kitchen stable door. 'Right-oh Stinkerbelle!' I said. 'Come and meet Chanok!' But she had already passed me, racing across the lawn to her shed. Chanok seeing her coming did a fast wriggly dive back into his holt. She stopped running, said 'Hah!' excitedly a couple of times, then swarmed slowly, carefully around the door, sniffing all the way. Suddenly Chanok put his head out and gave a loud, warning and spitty snort which made Stinkerbelle leap back and think twice about barging into her own shed where her own cage and blankets were being used as someone else's sleeping box. She took a little trip around the garden instead, trailing Chanok's scent over stones, around bushes, across the grass and around the pool. Evidently satisfied, back she went to the shed and put her head in again. 'Hah!' she said queryingly. 'Spit-snort!' went Chanok.

'Come on, lover boy,' I said. 'That's no way to treat your fate!' Stinkerbelle didn't withdraw this time, she barged in, rather unceremoniously I thought, and ignoring Chanok who was watching her with startled suspicion, began sniffing at his spraint tray and at her blankets with his scent on them. Then she went into her cage, sniffed at that and all the while Chanok was backing off from her and making small feinting gestures with his head, looking as frightened as any young rabbit, but determinedly snorting at her whenever she blundered too close to him.

'And goodness,' I thought, 'no wonder he's overcome. Why, she's twice the size he is! It's like seeing the fat lady at a circus with a pint-sized but bristly gent.' Suddenly, however, Chanok said 'Hah!' Stinkerbelle snubbed him. She seemed to be looking for another otter, maybe a bigger and lustier type. Evidently she didn't think much of Chanok as a mate proposition. She came back to my feet, rolled around and squeaked as if to say, Is that *all* you could get me? 'C'mon Stinkerbelle,' I said encouragingly, 'he'll grow!'

Chanok came out all in a rush and just about fell over backwards, because as soon as he saw Stinkerbelle he jerked to a stop. Stinkerbelle turned to look at him rather languidly and without much curiosity. I moved away. Chanok came forward; slowly, warily, sniffing towards her. She lumbered up and met him half way. Beside him she looked like a middle-aged matron with the appropriate spread. He didn't seem to think much of her either, for he gave another snort and retreated backwards into his shed again.

They gave up each other for a while, just sniffing at each other's traces. 'Well at least you didn't fight,' I said. 'Now Stinkerbelle, go and mother him then. Go *on!*' And she did.

It took him about half an hour or so to get over his fear and suspicion of her. They started circling on the lawn, Stinkerbelle always making sure my feet were in sight so that she could get between them for protection. I could never understand why Stinkerbelle was such a coward where strange otters were concerned and so beastly ferocious where people were. Actually I'd never known her to be anything but shy or fearful of, then positively charming to other otters, if they invitingly allowed her to be. She had a real sympathetic nature where other otters were concerned and I was very thankful for this admirable trait of hers.

They really got to know each other playing the circling game:

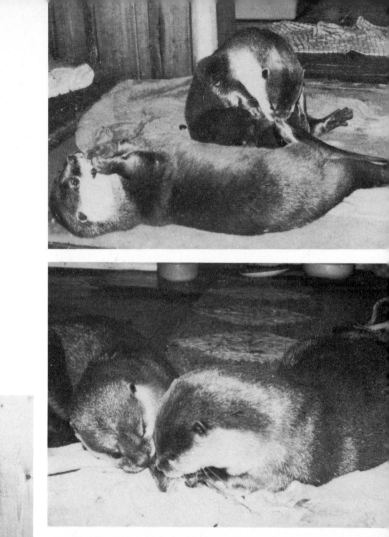

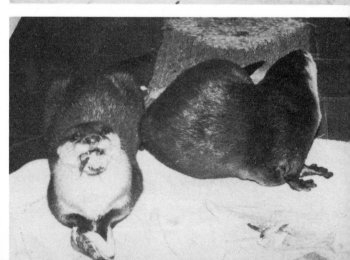

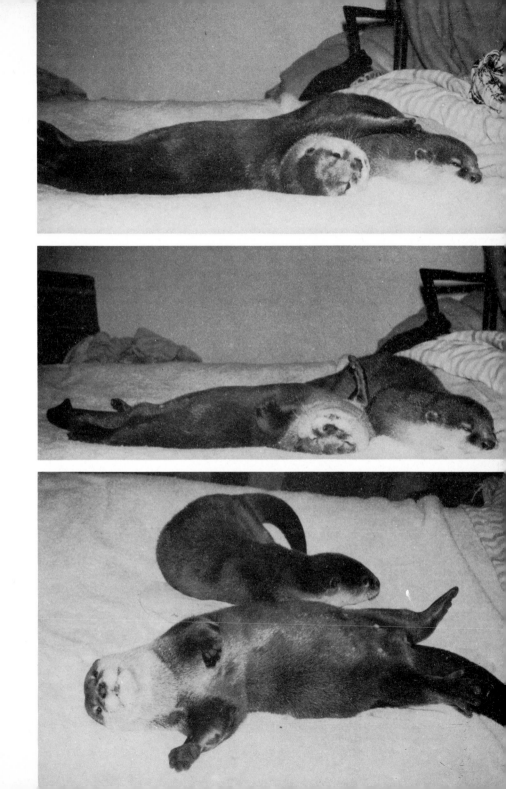

tentative sniffs and rather snake-like darting of heads, twisted a little in the process towards each other's necks, The head would shoot forward, sideways inclined, then recoil back making the neck thick again. A hesitation, then two bodies would curve towards each other, heads drawn back making folds of skin round the neck. Then for a second or two they'd be very still, watching each other, waiting. Another sudden dart and a change of position. Then at last, Chanok ran after her. She stopped, turned, let herself be sniffed, darted at him. He ran. She chased him. It was on.

I wished there could have been water in the pool but Chanok still had his stitches in so the pool was dry and Chanok kept bouncing in to it and putting his head over the top stones while Stinkerbelle made feints at him from above. Soon they were prancing at one another. First a short run, then Stinkerbelle would stop, turn slightly curved and as Chanok came head darting at her, she would stand up on her back feet, front paws held up, twist away from him, then down on her front paws and dart as he recoiled with a quick movement and pranced up too. For a split second they both would be up on their wide back feet, rudders helping the balance, an arching curve and counter curve as heads darted, recoiled, then off they were again, racing across the lawn.

After a while Stinkerbelle decided she'd have a little grooming session. Chanok decided to help her round the neck region. He probably bit a little too deeply for suddenly she yelp-squeaked at him and he backed off hurriedly, looking like any cub told to lay off by its mum. But soon he started playing with her tail and they were chasing one another once more.

It was marvellous to see two otters playing together again! I wasn't quite sure whether I was going to let them sleep together or not that evening. However, the question was decided for me. I'd left the inter-connecting doors open so they could dash up to the bedroom and play there if they wanted to. I watched Chanok following Stinkerbelle up the stairs and heard them scuffling away over the bed, through the chair and what have you. Then silence. I went up.

Two mounds at the bottom of my bed.

'Now look here, Stinkerbelle!' I said, rooting her out and watching

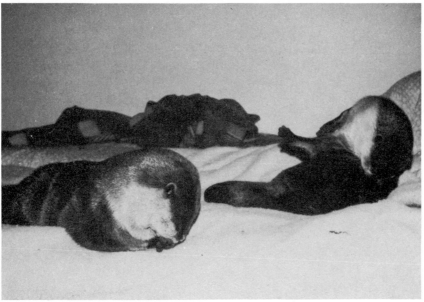

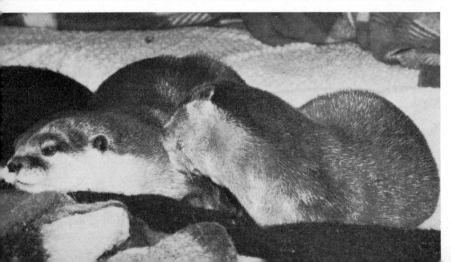

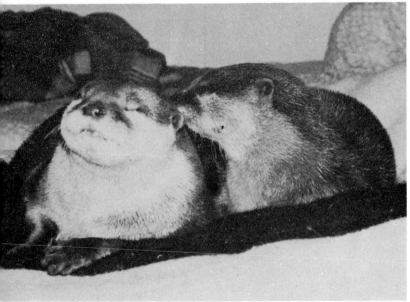

L

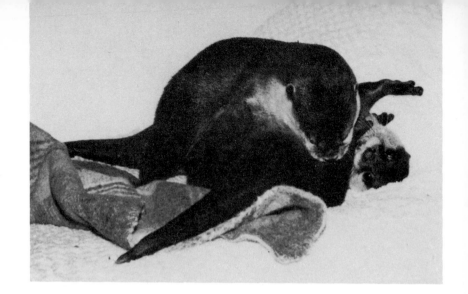

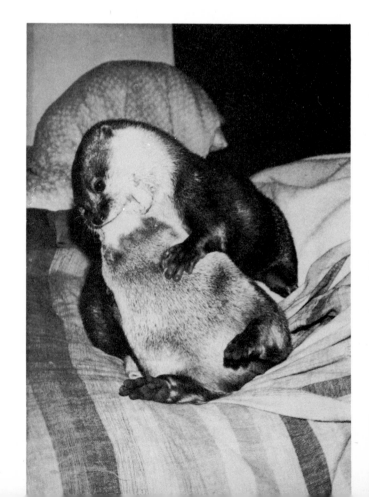

Chanok take a flying leap over the floor. 'Look here, that's *my* bed! Take him somewhere else, for goodness sake. He hasn't had a proper bath yet and God knows what . . . No! Not in there. Who left that drawer open! Here!' And I made up a blankety bed on the chair, tucked a spread well in over mine so they couldn't get in and watched them settle down again.

Chanok looked at me as if he'd just discovered I was there. He didn't find me interesting any more now he had Stinkerbelle for company. He clung to her, followed her about as she sniffed out the best, warmest, most comfortable place for herself. He jumped on her as she burrowed under her rugs and she growled at him, telling him to get off her back and behave himself. So he did, cuddling down around and on top of her on the big chair by the bed.

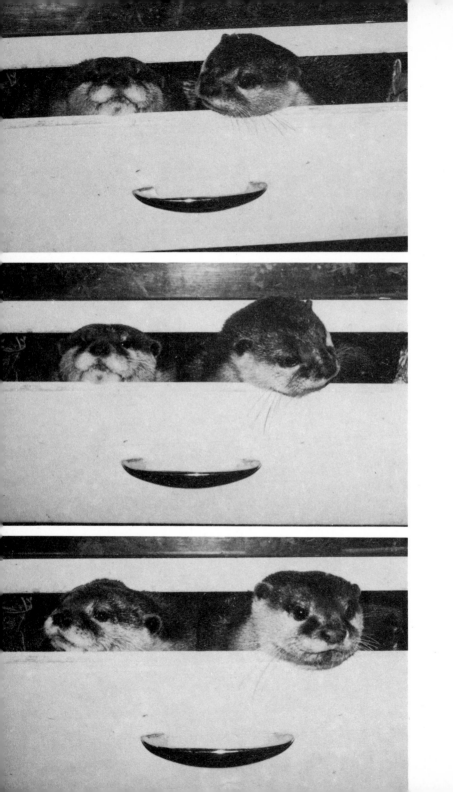

Stinkerbelle always burrowed and twisted herself so deeply into blankets that it was sometimes a job to unravel her. Chanok tried nudging and burrowing, but got another irritable growl for his pains, so he gave up after a while and went to sleep on top of the bulge she made. He kept one eye open which was fixed rather suspiciously, I thought, on me when I got into bed. He seemed to be wondering what on earth I was doing there. Every time I turned a page his head came up and his other eye opened. Finally he decided to investigate and I had his whiskery face peering at me over my book. Then he had a game, jumping on my toes and biting at them through the blankets if I wasn't quick enough to jerk them out of the way first.

This woke Stinkerbelle who swam out of her blankets, stretched, yawned widely, then deciding it was meal time, raced off downstairs, followed closely by Chanok, and began thumping the fridge door. I got out of bed, gave them both a very small snack and shut them in the kitchen while they were busy eating. I watched them through the glass door. A short play, then both went into the pot cupboard and curled up in the blankets there. I crept in to look at them once later that night. Chanok's head rose from the blanket and he snorted at me. He looked indignant, ready to do or die to defend his mate who, from the depths of her rugs, gave a short, irritated whine at being disturbed. All right Chanok, I said, you win. And added as I trundled off to bed, And thank heaven for that!

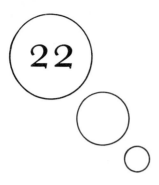

22

Yes, friends had said he was very keen on the idea of having otters, he had a suitable area of ground on which to have an enclosure and his civets and other animals had bred.

He lived a couple of hours' drive from London : a soft-spoken young man with a sympathetic air and a great interest in animals. I looked at his small collection, then looked at the proposed site for an otter enclosure. It certainly had possibilities; a grove of elm and hazel at one end, a small ditch across, a large area for pools, running and play-ing and for a sleeping shed.

It took some visualising at first because the whole area was covered in waist-high nettles, weed, thistle and blackberry. 'We'll clean and burn it off, dig it and sow grass,' he said enthusiastically as we slashed our way round its confines. 'It would make a very nice otter terrain,' I said.

The next week was spent on deciding how to build the enclosure. Telephone wires hummed and suggestions flew back and forth. We looked at new timber prices and quickly looked away again, at chain-link prices and paled at the prospect. Finally, after spending a few hours on the telephone I found a demolition yard somewhere between London and the proposed otter enclosure site.

We drove up, looked at the yard, talked to the helpful man there, chose our timbers and got the prices fixed.

We had decided to fence the enclosure using old floor board widths edge to edge. The fence height would be four foot six inches and we would use two four x two railings which would run along the outside of the vertical boards. The posts were outside the palings to allow no climbing grips inside – an inside-out fence as it were – the inside presenting the smooth surface of vertical planking.

The yard people trucked it up on a Saturday morning, together with sleepers and a load of hard-core and old bricks: this last was to make a mound into which we could fit the small fibre-glass pool from our garden so that its level would be higher than the large one to be brought from the little zoo where it still was. Two young boys who helped in the animal feeding and maintenance also worked very hard indeed. Hard-core had to be carted, timber cleaned up, the area dug over, posts set in and the paling wood cut into lengths and creosoted. But work progressed well; railings and palings were nailed up, sleepers aligned along the boundaries, and hard-core and cement laid wherever it looked as though there might be slight possibility of an otter digging out.

Meanwhile, back at home Chanok was getting very lively indeed. His stitches had come out, the wound had healed over and the shaved off patches were beginning to grow soft fur again. He was charming, friendly, a little on the defensive still, but had settled down and found that life could be really enjoyable. He loved playing with Stinkerbelle or, if she were not in the mood, eagerly organizing me as a stand-in. He liked chasing a soft rubber play ring which I'd attached to a long piece of string; great scrambles up and down stairs, then out through

the kitchen, around the garden and back again. He liked digging up the lawn, hunting for worms. He was a real wormer. The lawn digging didn't please me too much.

He especially enjoyed himself when he discovered that he could swim.

At first he stayed on the pool shelf, hanging on with his pliable back feet and just dipping his head and front paws into the depths. Stinkerbelle changed all that though. She peered over the top watching him for a while, then slid quietly down to the shelf and sat on his backside flattening out the poor little chap in the process. Then she arched round, grabbed a loose fold of skin round the neck, dragged him off the shelf and under. Good heavens! I thought, she'll drown him! There followed some frantic twisting and turning. He got halfway up onto the shelf again in shallower water, but she clasped him round the rump to pull him back in again. He did a quick dive, a flip round her and came out like a wriggly eel, highly excited now. He rolled and

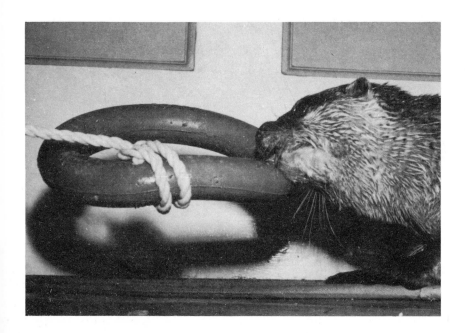

rolled and wriggled on his drying mat, then he went for another dip, carefully though, nosing the water first, taking his time about it until he heard Stinkerbelle pounding up behind him.

Soon he loved swimming, taking running dives off the edge or over the shelf, splashing in with great careless belly flops, turning, twisting, dolphining, then out again to chase Stinkerbelle around the garden until she chased him back. Another dash and he would take a running plunge into the pool, or a flat, high speed flop. Then as soon as he was back on the shelf, he would start an excited squealing, prancing on his back feet, tail swishing, beating the water from side to side while Stinkerbelle leant over the edge, feinting.

Then forward he would come, darting at her neck. She would rise in the prancing position, front paws held up as she arched sideways towards him. He would back off, tail swishing, doing that funny little dance again and squeaking at her. But suddenly she'd be on top of

170

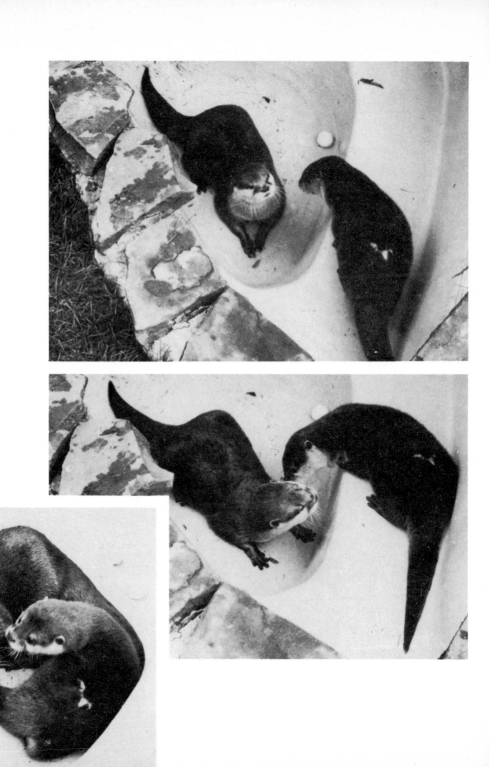

him, twisting him round, pushing him in order to take over the shelf and all the while he'd try to gain the advantage and get back up again. After a long play, when they were both hungry, Stinkerbelle would squeak loudly and Chanok would give a series of high, whinnying squeaks; his voice sounded as though it hadn't broken yet.

I watched them for a while before getting on with her feeding box. If Stinkerbelle hadn't wanted to bite everyone this would have been unnecessary, but since she did, I had to make one. At that point it was $51\frac{1}{8}$ inches x $52\frac{7}{8}$ inches and I couldn't quite understand where those extra eighths had come from. I certainly hadn't intended them to be there. In fact, I had only discovered them when I went to buy wood and the man said, 'Oh, you mean you want $1\frac{3}{4}$ x $\frac{5}{8}$ths.'

'Five-eighths?'

'Yeah, one over half inch, love.'

'Oh yes, well, I'll have it then.'

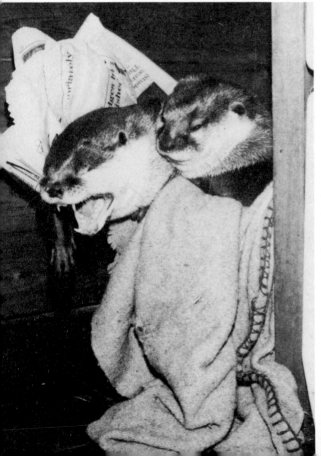

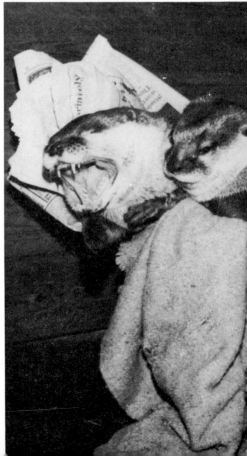

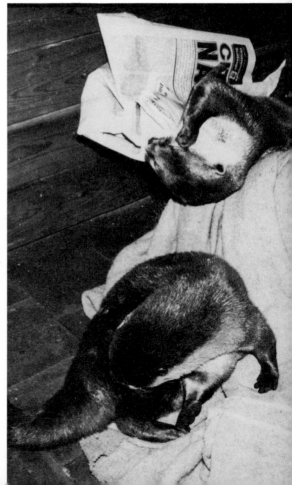

'Screws?'

'Oh, not those screws. They don't fit the electric drill. I mean, I can't change the drill piece, you see, because I don't know how to get it off.'

'Oh, you want a chuck then?'

'That's all I want. I mean – er – do I?'

So I got a chuck key, screws and bits of wood at lengths surprising to the do-it-yourself man. Then I set up a clamp in the kitchen, stood on the laundry box, drilled and after screwing the pieces up, found I couldn't get the frame out of the door, so I had to unscrew it all again.

But at last the completed frame was on the patio. The top and bottom would be covered with heavy ply and the sides with wire. The whole thing would fit outside and into the enclosure wall and doors at each end could be opened or closed by pulleys. The inner traps should be closed (when the otters were out, of course) before opening the outer ones to put in their food. With this done, the outer doors would be slid back into place, the inner ones pulled up and the otters could enter to eat.

After the otters had finished eating, the procedure would be reversed and the cleaning-up could be done, especially in summer when flies would probably descend on any left-over fish. Two small water bowls would be in there too. I intended putting thick rubberized lino on the floor to make it easier to swish over with a sponge mop and disinfectant from time to time. Otters in the wild, eating freshly caught fish and moving over large areas, aren't subject to fly-carried disease, or the effects of bits of fish or meat left rotting around. In captivity, however, one couldn't be too careful about the freshness of their food, clean water and, above all, scrupulously clean eating areas, bowls and so on.

I was still working out the feeding box problem when Forbes finally arrived back.

I met him at the airport. He'd had a long flight, practically non-stop from Pacific regions, but looked very fit. We had got so much to tell each other that we were still chattering away as we entered the house.

It was about midnight. Stinkerbelle and Chanok were asleep in the pot cupboard but as soon as we got through the door, she woke up, heard him, said 'Hah!' loudly, excitedly and came leaping out. 'Hah!' said Forbes happily back; 'Hah!' said Stinkerbelle.

She was so worked up she hardly knew what to do with herself at first. Then after another 'Hah!' she pushed between his feet demanding attention. He bent down to stroke her and talk to her. She responded, lay on her back, but was up again in a minute, sniffing his feet, his legs. He stroked her again. She was sniffing at his hands when suddenly I felt tension in the air. The next second, with an attack scream, she bit.

She had Forbes's hand in her teeth. I grabbed her, carried her back into the kitchen and shut the glass door firmly between us. She stood there screaming abuse. Chanok came out, blinking, looking confused.

I went back into the kitchen, quietened her down, took her blankets over the garden to the outside shed, the spraint tray, then some food. They settled down out there. She was munching away unconcernedly at her fish as I shut the back door.

Forbes and I looked at each other in silence, rather desperately. We fixed some sticking plaster over a couple of small holes around his knuckles. Then we both took to a drink. 'We'll try again in the morning,' said Forbes.

We gave up after a few minutes though, for she screamed so loud and volubly that we decided not to try direct communication. She had made it quite clear what her intentions were. That she had recognised him was certain, but that she would not accept his presence in the house was absolutely clear. Every time she saw him, she attack-screamed. If she came into a room where he had recently been, she would sniff at the chair he'd been sitting on, scuff furiously around in it and scream again. If she came across any of his clothes she would do the same thing. If she heard him she would show her annoyance. It was unpleasant for all of us and I wondered what the neighbours and people for a couple of blocks down the street thought.

Happily she could easily be partitioned off, due to the system of doors and dog hole so cohabitation wasn't as difficult as it might have been, but there was no doubt that she had become so suspicious of any human who might present a threat to her security, that on seeing Forbes she was fully determined to oust him.

We tried taking her for walks together, but even in the park she would scream at him. She would allow other men to pass quite close to her with hardly a glance, but if Forbes showed up even yards away, myopic as she was, she would immediately recognise the way he moved. Sometimes she would let him walk or sit down about fifteen yards from us, but this was very rare.

Worse, she began trying to search him out in the house, trying to wriggle round doors to get at him. She was determined about it, was Stinkerbelle, and as we had both been looking forward to going on long walks together with her, it made it all very sad.

Chanok had a great time though, for when I took Stinkerbelle alone out for a walk he would get extra play sessions with Forbes who found him charming.

Meanwhile Stinkerbelle was getting bigger in the lower regions; her nipples showed really red and quite large. If she were going to have cubs then it was almost time for her to drop them. I still took her on shortened versions of our early morning walks, however, carefully lifting her into the bicycle basket and handling her gently, until one day in the park she started to crawl instead of gallop. She lay down, groaned, crawled into my lap and lay there panting for all the world as if she were in the last stages. 'Good God!' I thought. 'She's about to drop them!' As gently as possible I carried her back home and settled her in her comfy sleeping quarters in the garden shed.

'She *must* be!' I said to Forbes.

'Look, why don't we take her to the local vet and get her X-rayed to be quite sure,' he suggested.

We did.

She seemed to have got over her languid, crawling stage, but behaved well and quietly for the X-ray technician and vet. When the results came through there was not a *sign* of a cub!

'Stinkerbelle, you fraud!' we said sending her off to Chanok with a flea in her ear and a promise of a strict diet.

It seemed she had gone through a false pregnancy. Some dogs do this, even humans are known to have them. Stinkerbelle as well as *looking* as though she were going to drop cubs at any minute, certainly must have felt as if she were going to have them. After that day in the park and her false delivery she lost weight again, got more bouncy and playful and less like an about-to-be-mother of six.

Meanwhile Forbes applied his science to the feeding box and made a great job of it. I was doubly thankful he had managed to get back at this time. Then we went up and helped with the enclosure preparations. Mrs Howard, our marvellous neighbour said, 'Now you two take my car and I'll feed Stinkerbelle and Chanok over the fence and see to the parrots.'

The sleeping shed had been set up by the two boys and lined with straw. It had an infra-red heating lamp for severe wintry days and there was room inside for Stinkerbelle's sleeping cage and also her dog basket. It had, besides a door for humans, a slot door on a pulley for otters. They could be shut in there for short periods if necessary.

We lined the ditch and checked the grills set in concrete at each end and dug in the two fibre glass pools. Paving stones went around them and water from the smaller top one cascaded over into the large one from which a pipe led into the ditch. The water supply was brought by hose and hung over a small tree by the top pool so that the water could hose down into it. Grass was sown, a play area from the sleeping shed to the food box was roofed so that in the cold months ahead they would have a place to get dry and play before going into their holt. Big logs were put near the pool and it all looked very nice and natural. Everyone had worked very hard.

We decided to let a couple of weeks go by to give the grass time to take hold. Forbes had a conference in Noumea before he had to return to Suva and this allowed me time to pack up and get the otters settled before joining him.

'Well, Stinkerbelle,' said Forbes as he left, 'everything's laid on for you, behave yourself now!' For once she didn't scream at him. 'Keep her under control, Chanok,' said Forbes and off he flew to New Caledonia.

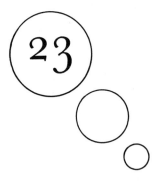

23

The grass seed started to sprout.

Mrs Howard had offered to take Jacka and Oskar while I was away. 'Are you sure?' I asked. 'I'd love to look after them,' she said. So while the grass was growing up north we made an aviary in her back porch and settled Jacka and Oskar in there. They had an outside cage as well into which they could fly from the open window. There were plenty of perches, a shelf with logs on and various other chewy bits and pieces. The porch had a glass roof, one wall was window and it was light, sunny and a marvellous place for them. 'But I say,' I said, 'it rather takes over your back porch, doesn't it?'

'Don't worry I don't use it much and I love having them. They look so pretty in it!'

It was strange at first to hear Jacka and Oskar whistling next door. I could look over the fence and see them in their aviary where they looked very content, preening in the sunshine. With lots of flying space there was room enough for Jacka to avoid Oskar's bully tactics. I could hear Mrs Howard talking to them in the morning sometimes and of course I went over often to talk to them myself. I was very happy that someone so kind to animals should be looking after them and enjoying the experience.

And the grass was growing. It was time to take the otters up to their new home. I took Stinkerbelle out in the park for three hours the day before: a lovely sunny day. She caught frogs, sticklebacks and rolled and galloped and swam and we sat in our favourite resting place and

looked at familiar scenes and I thought a bit and watched Stinkerbelle
get duck weed over one eye and hoped she would happily settle down
to her new life.

My neighbour and I drove up with Chanok and Stinkerbelle curled
up together in Stinkerbelle's cage. The car was piled with food, bowls,
ice bucket of fish, sponge mats, toys, their sleeping rugs and covers,
spraint trays and other otter luggage.

We took the cage into the enclosure where I opened the door and
let them out. Water was falling into the top pool with a nice sound,
then cascading over smooth paving stones and into the lower pool.
The two otters began to explore, sniffing around the periphery of the
enclosure or digging under logs, until both dived into the top pool,
splashed down into the large one, then over from that for a run along
the ditch.

Their sleeping shed was organized with the cosy sleeping cage and
basket stuffed with covers. The sponge mat was laid down as a drying

mat just outside. Lino was put in the feeding box, then the food and water put in, the outside door reshut and the inside ones pulleyed open.

As they were familiar with the box, having closely followed its progress from the beginning in the patio at home, it didn't take them very long to get used to it and come to expect their food there. We watched them playing and decided they looked very content wrestling together, bounding over the grass, or scuffing in their sand pit.

Later that night we went back to check them. A bright moon shone above the dark silhouettes of trees, reflections on water, paving stones gleamed white and Stinkerbelle and Chanok were squeaking to each other as they went on a night prowl. Then a splash in the pool; a glimpse of them chasing each other across the grass, then back again up the pool side, and another splash as they hit the water again. We withdrew quietly.

In between packing, I made frequent trips to see how they were getting on and found them making the most of life in their large new home. They were receiving excellent care and attention and everyone was pleased with them.

The second time I went up, I decided to hammer in an extra slat

of wood along the edge of their sleeping shed. Stinkerbelle was behind me. The hammering annoyed her and for the first time in her life she made a bite at my leg which was rather cramped up between sleeping box and wall. 'Stinkerbelle!' I raged. 'You little . . . ' Then had to laugh. She looked so shocked and shamefaced about it, lying on her back submissively groaning, asking for forgiveness. Her teeth hadn't gone through the skin, but I scolded her before stroking her.

I spent a few more hours in the enclosure with them, playing and feeding them and generally enjoying their company. Chanok was certainly in his element. He'd never had such a large play area before and never such an expanse of water to swim in.

The next time I called and went into the enclosure, Stinkerbelle greeted me, then gave a short screech and bit me on the leg. I growled at her ferociously and picked her up, still growling. Then I sat and talked to her, reassured her out of her submissive state and chatted and played with them both.

My leg bled a little, but they were puncture bites in the soft part of the calf which didn't hurt or otherwise give further trouble. Stinkerbelle seemed nervous during the day. I cleaned out the pools since I was there in the enclosure and it would save the boys their Saturday task. I noticed, however, that every now and then she would tense and make those peculiar, small, slightly whining squeaks which meant possible trouble.

Every time she did this I picked her up, at which she got submissive again and I was able to calm her down. She had lost some weight which she well needed to do, but was in very good condition; indeed they both were. Chanok was growing fast; both their coats looked glossy and shone in the sunlight. But often she had a slightly worried look on her face and although we hadn't lost contact, I felt that sooner or later we would and was fairly pleased about this. It would mean that she would become more dependent on Chanok and he wouldn't take long, at the rate he was growing, to get to her size and satisfaction.

Before I left, I stood outside the enclosure behind some trees and watched them. After feeling sure that I had gone, Stinkerbelle sniffed around for a while, then she and Chanok started playing together,

184

chasing one another, swimming, then rolling themselves dry. They raced along the ditch, sometimes one of them along the top following the other rushing along the bottom. They were certainly content together and I left them to it.

The last time I went to see them it was to wave goodbye for my flight was booked and I was packed and ready to fly off to the Pacific. It was perhaps silly to go into the enclosure, but she had greeted me over the fence with her usual excited Hah! sounds. I had purposely put on an old pair of slacks and left them hanging over my gumboots, for I knew she might bite me, but I hoped that by picking her up again I could calm her. Besides, I wanted to check her teeth.

I 'hah-ed!' at her, then went in, talked to her and picked her up when she got tense and made those little menacing sniffs and squeaks again. I opened her mouth, examined her teeth for calculus deposits, then put her down, walked around with her, greeted Chanok, groomed him and turned back to Stinkerbelle.

But there was no feeling of contact. It's hard to describe this and how it differed from all other times. I can only say the wave length between us had been broken. Great distances seemed to be separating us; nor did I feel any fear of her, since having lived with her so long this simply did not come into it. In fact, I felt rather vague and a bit sad.

I put down my hand to stroke her again and it was then she attacked it. She also attack-screamed. Had it been a strange otter I think I probably would have kicked her. Then, when she turned on my foot, I could have grabbed her tail in order to lift her off the ground for this always took the wind out of her sails. I could have then thrown her some distance across the grass which would have given me time to get out. But as it was Stinkerbelle-the-Nark, it didn't occur to me to kick her.

Instead, I prised her jaws open to free my left hand and as soon as I did this she grabbed my right. I spoke to her sharply, called her name, did my lion-like roar at her, but it didn't sound too convincing. For a little while both of us danced around the enclosure. Stinkerbelle was screaming her head off, I was swearing volubly and trying things like dunking her into the pool and holding her under until she had to gasp for air and let go.

My hands were getting somewhat punctured and I wondered, as I forced open her mouth again only to have the forcing hand snapped into and held in needle-like vice, how on earth I was going to outwit her. I didn't feel any pain though, curious phenomenon this. I really believe now that animals when attacked don't feel pain, for their whole being is concentrated on defence or escape. I did finally get her off my hands and on to my gumboot which she proceeded to bite holes out of and generally enjoy. By this time however I was on top of the fence and, managing to get my foot out of the boot, I was only too glad to let her have it. She hadn't bitten through to my legs, But as soon as I sat down and began thinking about my hands, they became rather painful, for although the bites were not very deep, one has plenty of nerves in one's fingers.

Stinkerbelle meanwhile was squeaking plaintively on the other side of the fence. 'All right, you little *nark!*' I said and she had the utter cheek to say 'Hah!' to me. Chanok during all this had been looking on with much bewilderment.

It was not what one might have called the happiest sort of farewell, but again I was glad that as a pair they were independent; human contact or attachment was no longer necessary to their well-being, and notwithstanding all the trouble and worry in which she had involved me, the result had been worth it. If I had lost a companion – mischievous, narky, amusing, interesting, affectionate, in a word, wholly absorbing – I had gained an insight into her world and a deeper understanding of animals as cognizant beings, their need of space, activity and independence.

One cannot accuse Stinkerbelle of being ungrateful. If you think about it, as I have done often, one must come to the conclusion that there is a kind of justice in her rejection of humans, including myself.

I watched the two otters move off together towards the pools. Chanok groomed her solicitously, she responded to him, and soon the pair dived from the rocky edge and into their pool. I moved away then. 'Goodbye Chanok, goodbye Stinkerbelle-my-Nark,' I said and finally walked away without looking back.

All photographs are by the author except the following which are reproduced by kind permission of Cassidy and Leigh: pages 6, 9, 15 (*bottom*), 19, 102 and 107.